Also by James Nelson

The Trouble With Gumballs

Great Cheap Wines,
a Poorperson's Guide

Everybody's Guide to
Great Wines Under $5

Killing
Dave Henderson,
etc...

Killing Dave Henderson, etc...

James Nelson

RDR Books
Muskegon / Berkeley

RDR Books
1487 Glen Avenue, Muskegon, MI 49441
Phone: (510) 595-0595   Fax: (510) 228-0300
Website: www.rdrbooks.com   E-mail: read@rdrbooks.com

The Trouble With Ada previously appeared in *Chatelaine*, c/o Rogers Media, Ltd., Canada

Elect the Healthiest previously appeared in *The Atlantic Monthly*

Killing Dave Henderson previously appeared in *Smithsonian* under the title *Dave Henderson Was Becoming an Embarrassment*

My Private War With Herman previously appeared in *The Philadelphia Inquirer Sunday Magazine*

April 14th in Fry's Landing previously appeared in *Good Housekeeping*

Photograph and script excerpt from *Grand Canyon* © 1991 20th Century Fox, written by Lawrence and Meg Kasdan. All rights reserved.

Book and cover design by John De Bonis
Cover photograph by Pach Brothers, New Haven
Back cover photograph by Rebecca Sylla
Page preparation by Phoenix Word & Press

Printed in the United States of America

Library of Congress Control Number: 2006928589

ISBN 978- 1-57143-164-6

For my pal,
Mary-Armour...

...and for Jackson, Randa, Nina, Tyler,
Will, Eli, and Cameron

CONTENTS

Part One: Killing Dave...

Part Two: Etc...

Part Three: Partners in Crime

"Oh, that my words were already written down,

Oh, that they were printed in a book."

—Job, 19:23

Part One: Killing Dave...

Meeting Dave Henderson

In June of 1981 I celebrated, which is the wrong word, ten years as a Class Agent for the Yale Alumni Fund. I'd been merciless in urging my Classmates to give, give, give. But I was tired of the job. I began to hate adding a cheery little handwritten P.S. to each letter. I figured it was someone else's turn.

I can't remember how I dragooned another innocent guy into taking the job. But, miracles do happen. I handed my records over to him, gave him a pat on the back, and settled down for a long nap.

I didn't nap long. As it turned out, there was another guy who was tired. He was the guy who wrote our Class Notes for the *Alumni Magazine*. He wanted out. He figured it was someone else's turn. He wondered if I wouldn't like to do it.

He didn't present it to me like that, of course. No, he said it was a lot of fun. He said I'd have a ball. It wasn't like collecting money. It was easy. It was mainly editing. Hadn't I been an editor at *Business Week?* Well, our classmates would send me their news, and all I would have to do was give it a light editing and shoot it off to be printed. Piece of cake.

I took the bait. I'm not sorry I did. It wasn't a piece of cake, but I enjoyed doing it. I did it faithfully for six years, during which time I became extremely well acquainted with a classmate I'd never met during my college years. His name was Dave Henderson.

I liked Dave, and as time went by, I came to know the rest of his family. They were an interesting bunch, and I appreciated it when Dave would send me some tidbit of news about them for the '43 Class Notes. Little did I know that, before my job ended, Dave would be dead, and Carter Wiseman, the Editor of the *Yale Alumni Magazine,* would be frothing at the mouth.

Carter saw Dave in a completely different light. Once he got to know him, he hated him. Thus, when I begged him to let me include Dave's obituary in the pages of the *Alumni Magazine*, he refused. Flatly. Flatter than flatly.

I decided, therefore, to write up Dave's history, including his obituary, and see if I couldn't get someone else to publish it. When I finished my piece I sent it off to Al Hart, my gentleman/scholar/agent in New York, and Al, in turn, sent it to *Smithsonian Magazine.* Happily, *Smithsonian* liked the story and ran it as it appears in the following pages, under the title, *"Dave Henderson Was Becoming an Embarrassment."*

I call it, *"Killing Dave Henderson."*

l
e
et
as

of
ided
l the
ients,
eports
nming
ianges.
human
abit and
u is now

and Peru,
, and was
m's names
ian (former
ition him by
n 1988. **Phil**
n recognition
founder of the
roup of retired
volunteer serv-
, in health care,
and the arts.
:, from whom I
tting his inability
med from Mexico

Lastly, you sh... reunion will have as its chai... ay "chairpersons" but can't bring mysel... and **Turner** (reunion), **Twigg-Smith** (50th Fund) and **Ewald** (yearbook). A great team and Twigg is already at work—get out your checkbooks!

Send me in some news items, especially those of you who haven't been so vocal.

George Pillsbury, Secretary
1300 TCF Tower, Minneapolis, MN 55402
by **Jim Nelson,** Corresponding Secretary
649 Idylberry Rd., San Rafael, CA 94903
John M. Thornton, Asst. Cor. Secretary
Box 15, R.D.4, Sewickley, PA 15143

43

I'm happy to report from the West Coast that a few late starters are heating up the Grandparent Sweepstakes again. Perhaps it has been triggered by lingering envy of **Bob Berry,** who back in '86 set the record with eleven grandchildren, or perhaps by the report of the birth of **Lou Nickell**'s first *great*-grandchild. In any event, from San Jose, Calif., **Bob Terrill** reports: "First entry in the Grandchild Derby born eighteen months ago—the Terrills clone themselves but thrice a century. Had a mild cardiac in May of '87— angioplasty—and now leading a low-cal, energetic life. Should be around for our 50th Reunion."

Other first-time grandparents include **Bliss Woodruff,** who reports the arrival of David Miller Woodruff II on April 30, and **Innis O'Rourke,** announcing Innis IV, born May 17, both in 1988. Your two Corresponding Secretaries make up the final two sets of hyperexcited first-time grandparents, with Elizabeth and **Jake Thornton** reporting the arrival of Benjamin James Thornton on October 12, while Mary-Armour and **Jim Nelson,** the guy writing the notes this time, report that on December 28 their daughter Marie-Louise presented the world with Jackson Charles Masters.

From Santa Fe, N. Mex., **Frank Lee** writes: "I expect to have a second grandchild on my mother's ... were she alive . . . Ruth and I jus... day trip to China, Hon... the Chi...

writes: "We sp...
in Europe last sum
on the Middle East
sity's beautiful L
annual conferenc
Strategic Studies
wife and I visi
50th reunion at
Though still pr
tage of Yale,
terioration of
my old haur
from **Jack**
twenty-two
was a fancy
and 'Curre
ect to dat
5-year-ol
From
retired i
ruple b
more th
ican P
with c
lar ir
supp
then
Sar
wi
ex
sh
v

Killing Dave Henderson

Smithsonian, March 1991

I didn't want to kill Dave Henderson. Though I didn't know him well, I had grown surprisingly fond of him. For six years, I excerpted his many newsy and colorful letters for inclusion in the class notes column that appears in each issue of the *Yale Alumni Magazine*. I had, in fact, taken a certain vicarious pleasure in his opulent and sometimes slippery escapades. The powers that be, however, did not share my feelings. Henderson was becoming an embarrassment to his—and my—university.

Dave hadn't always been such a thorn in Yale's side. In fact, during the first 41 years following the graduation of the class of '43, Dave left Yale entirely alone. *Lux et Veritas* was nothing to him, it appeared. No one in the class reported hearing from him; he sent no news to the class secretaries, and he sent no money to the alumni fund. Moreover, when it came time to bring out a new 1943 class directory, Dave didn't even bother to send along his address.

It was as if he didn't even exist.

It was not until early 1984, in fact, 18 months after I'd taken on the task of assembling class notes for the *Alumni Magazine*, that anyone heard from Dave.

His first message came in the form of a short post-card from Mexico. Dutifully—and more or less innocently—I included the following in my column:

Writing from his winter home in Cancún, DAVE HENDER-SON reports that his company finally lost its long bout with Chapter Eleven. Says Dave philosophically, "I didn't really mind—I was sick and tired of trying to breathe life into the damned thing!" Dave says he had several pleasant conversations with two class members he met at the Betty Ford Institute last fall.

A month later a second communication from Dave appeared. This time his tone was more mellow, and he extended the first of many hospitable invitations to his classmates, indicating, I felt, his desire to rejoin our world. I included it in the June 1984 issue:

From Cartagena, Colombia, DAVE HENDERSON writes: "Marge and I flew down to the boat early this year to escape the Mexican heat. We plan to cruise the East Coast of South America for awhile, but we'll be back home in Cancún by October first, with plenty of Margaritas and spare bedrooms for all visiting '43-ers...'

Early that fall, I had another note from Dave. Before I give it to you, though, a few words about class notes in general. As everyone knows, they are a very popular item in every alumni magazine. No matter how relevant or flashy the editors try to make their lead articles, the first thing alumni turn to—if they turn to anything at all—is the back of the book where the class notes are buried. The habit is so addictive that people often find themselves reading about the lives of classmates they've never met or about alumni in other classes. Hard-core class notes junkies even read about the alumni of other schools. I've heard of a man, 40 years on, who for some reason still keeps track of the doings of his wife's Wellesley classmates, a number of whom he used to date.

But if your class notes are anything like mine, in a class of 850 there are 25 active, extroverted, well-placed members whose names seem to appear in the column—in boldface—in each and every issue. There are also 825 normal folk, drudges and geniuses alike, whose names, since graduating, have appeared once or, more likely, not at all. This isn't elitism on the part of the class notes secretary. Several times a year, every member of the class is encouraged, nay hectored, to send in news of himself or other classmates. The 825 average Joes (and where applicable, Jills) ignore the request. The active, voluble 25, on the other hand, send in their news. And send, and send, and send.

The nature of the news, of course, has something to do with it. If you've just been named to the boards of three Fortune 500 companies and your youngest son has reached the quarter-finals at Wimbledon, you're a bit more likely to send your news in than if you've been in the same nothing job for 29 years and your kids are still tie-dyeing T-shirts.

To be perfectly honest, a principal reason I took on the class notes job was to search for the silent 825. I wanted to hear about what they were doing. Thus, I sent out flight after flight of letters, trying to pry news from them. To classmates I knew, I made the letters personal. Others I tried to stir into action by referring to some item from our class book, published at the time of our graduation more than 40 years ago. "Do you still fence?" I would ask. "Have you kept up your interest in drama?" "Do they still call you 'Stumpie'?"

As a further incentive, I included a self-addressed, stamped envelope, in the deluded hope that my Yale classmates, moved by the appeal, would instantly scribble a few lines and mail them off. No dice. For every 20 letters sent out, I got back—well, maybe 2. There are days, indeed, with deadline near and copy short, when a class secretary may feel a strong urge to invent. In any case, had a few more of the uncommunicative 825 replied to my requests, Dave Henderson might never have turned up in the *Alumni Magazine*. And I, as a result, would not have been compelled to take his life.

His November 1984 note, unlike his first, was as lively as could be:

"Back in Cancún earlier than expected, thanks (no thanks!) to Marge and self having been put under 'boat arrest' for ten days in S. João do Monte, a tiny port town north of Recife (east coast of Brazil) for suspected trafficking in 'illegal substances.' The whole thing was poppycock, of course, and ended only after we gave a lavish party on the boat for the entire police department, their wives, girlfriends, and God-knows-who-else! The incident shook us up, nevertheless, and we flew home, leaving the crew to take our boat back to Cartagena. Still hoping some '43-ers will look us up in Cancún this winter."

Dave's messages kept coming. It was as though, having finally pulled the stopper from the bottle, he couldn't keep the contents from gushing forth.

April 1985:

From even further south—south of the border, in fact—DAVE HENDERSON sends several color photos of his fabulous Cancún home, together with the following note: "Marge and I plan to have the whole family here for Easter, provided the court will modify the terms of our daughter Sondra's parole to permit her a brief trip out of the U.S. If she gets turned down, we'll gather instead at the Plaza for a week, in which case I'll hope to catch up with a few venerable New York '43-ers whom I haven't seen since New Haven days. Incidentally, watch for Sondra's book, Triplecross!, *which will be out in September. I believe it will cause quite a stir in the intelligence-gathering community..."*

June 1985:

Heading west across the Caribbean to Cancún, Mexico, we have this report from DAVE HENDERSON: "I hope none of my classmates gave credence to the recent and extremely scurrilous Wall Street Journal story about the demise of my company. In spite of the fact that they didn't actually use my name, I found their raking of coals now dead for nearly two years both unnecessary and reprehensible. Their further gall in printing a totally unfounded rumor that certain senior officers had delayed the Chapter Eleven filing until they could siphon off the assets represents the most irresponsible kind of yellow journalism! A pox on them! On a much happier note, Marge and I plan to fly to Italy and spend the entire month of June aboard our boat, Triunfador*</p>

II. We'll be anchored a great many nights at Portofino, and would be happy to have any touring members of '43 who find themselves in that lovely spot come aboard for a drink or a meal. . ."

Apparently no one showed up in Portofino. At least Dave did not mention a reunion in any of the letters that followed the Mediterranean trip, such as this one from February 1986:

Received a note and a wedding snapshot from DAVE HENDERSON, wintering in his palatial home in Cancún, Mexico: "Just back from a quick trip to Paris to attend our daughter Karen's wedding to Attilo Katakunle, number three

man in Zaire's Ministry of Tourism. This is Karen's third
marriage, and we are hopeful that Attilo's sense of humor
and impressive good looks—he's 6'7", 290 pounds—mean
that he is Mr. Right for her... They will go to Zaire in late
spring for the birth of their child in the capital city of
Kinshasa (formerly Leopoldville), following which they
will journey to the interior to spend a month in Attilo's
village where, as nephew of the Chief, he is regarded as
royalty."*

After a longer than usual silence, I received the following
report of the Hendersons' hectic life:

*Finally, from Cancún, Mexico, DAVE HENDERSON writes:
"A busy winter with many visitors. Burt Lancaster was with
us for a long weekend while starring in a TV miniseries
being shot in Mexico City. He was followed by Imelda
Marcos and her entourage, who stayed nearly ten days.
Having Imelda as a guest is always quite an operation.
Her security people arrive a week early to check out the
premises and environs, and when Herself arrives, she comes
complete with personal secretary, maid, hairdresser, three
bodyguards, and a driver!" The driver, Tony, occasionally
doubles as a gourmet cook. This time Tony had just returned
from a refresher course in Evasive Driving Technique at
the Bob Bondurant School of High Performance Driving
near Sonoma, Cal. He gave us a demonstration using our
stretch limo, which he spun around as though it were a
sports car!"*

Dave's letter concluded, as always, with an open invitation
to his classmates:

"Incidentally, Marge and I are still hoping a few '43s will find their way here this spring for a week, a weekend, or whatever, plus some pleasant reminiscing ..."

Not long after Imelda's sojourn, the Marcoses' position in the Philippines deteriorated considerably. In a subsequent issue, Dave commented: *"You can imagine the shock Marge and I feel over what has happened since Imelda's visit to us last December!... After all that she and Ferdie did for the Philippine people, it seems their ingratitude knows no bounds!"*

I was beginning to wonder if Dave's classmates had taken any notice of his letters or of his invitations. Certainly by now *someone* should have contacted me to ask for Dave's address. Even if he hadn't been well known as a student, I thought his recent letters should have piqued his classmates' interest just a little. Apparently, however, his activities had not been sufficiently remarkable to cause a second thought.

In December 1986, I printed the following:

Enclosing a color snapshot of his 54-room palacio in Cancún, Mexico, DAVE HENDERSON writes: "Marge and I are heartsick that in July, pirates boarded our motor-yacht Triunfador II as it was passing through Malacca Straits, stripped it clean, and then opened the sea valves, sending the most comfortable cruiser we ever owned to the bottom of the sea. Two of the crew were killed scuffling with the boarding party, and the remaining ten were put off in lifeboats with little water and no food. They drifted 36 hours before being rescued. Fortunately, Marge and I had disembarked in Dar es Salaam and flown back to Johannesburg to check on some of our investments. We are now battling with our Panamanian insurance company about the sinking—they claim it was an act of God! Meanwhile, in Kobe, Japan, we have laid the keel for a new, much larger vessel. We hereby officially issue an invitation to all '43-ers in the area to attend the party when Triunfador III comes down the ways, God willing, in July of '87..."

Shortly after this note appeared, I received the letter I had been waiting for. A classmate wrote, wondering why he had been unable to locate Dave's name in the most recent class directory. But that was the only inquiry. "Who is Dave Henderson?" did not seem to be a fiercely burning question for the members of the class of '43.

If the readership of the *Yale Alumni Magazine* had been limited to Yale alumni, Henderson's little notes to his classmates clearly would have caused no stir. But when one of his letters was reprinted in the *San Francisco Chronicle* the pot began to boil. The letter appeared in the daily column of the *Chronicle's* venerated Herb Caen, under the title "Monday's Mildewed Memos." The item opened with the words "Dave Henderson has it made!" after which it quoted a letter from Dave, word for word as it had appeared in the *Alumni Magazine*:

> *I have a long letter from DAVE HENDERSON, with pictures of the launching of his new boat, Triunfador III. Says Dave, "Our shiny new putt-putt was to have been 163 feet overall, but after Marge's father kicked the bucket last year, we figured we could go another 30-40 feet. So, we redid the whole plan, and now it's 197 feet stem-to-stern, fitted out with every electronic marvel known to man, and furnished like a Sultan's harem! I feel like a kid with a new toy, and so does Marge! The other day she walked into the owner's suite—the whole thing's done in white-on-white—collapsed on the bed, and began to cry, she was so happy! Incidentally, we've got a wonderful new chef on board, and we're heading for Italy and the Cote d'Azur in May. Any '43-ers who spot us in one of the harbors in that neighborhood are hereby invited to come aboard for drinks and some of Andre's gourmet chow..."*

Caen closed with the comment, "Hold the Boola Boola soup, Andre, and pass the Mothersills—I'm afraid I'm feeling a bit queasy."

Soon thereafter, a concerned Yale graduate wrote Yale president

Benno C. Schmidt jr. and enclosed a copy of the Caen column. The letter commented, first, on the poor taste exhibited by the Hendersons in lengthening *Triunfador III* by 34 feet as a direct result of the death of Marge's father and, second, on Dave's even poorer taste in writing about it. Implicit was a third comment—on the notes secretary's poor taste for having included the item, and on the *Alumni Magazine's* for having printed it.

A short time later, Dave's letter gained a national audience. The *New Yorker* reprinted it as a column filler under the provocative heading "Department of Life Styles (Old Eli Division)." This time Dave's letter had company, a note from the Yale class of '44 concerning one Larry Vaughn.

Vaughn sounded as if he might have been a good friend of Dave's. For one thing, he had been canny enough to get out of the market before the October '87 crash. For another, he had left his wife, Claudine and daughter Fleur at their comfortable villa in Porto Cervo, Sardinia, while he spent two years high in the Himalayas, in Nepal's Chonro Lamasery, where, he reported, he was finding himself anew and meditating on the future.

Larry Vaughn shared another important characteristic with Dave Henderson. I could not find his name in the *Yale Alumni Directory.*

This odd coincidence did not surprise me. Though I'd never heard of Larry Vaughn, I'd already learned that David Henderson was not as unique as he seemed. A few months earlier, my wife and I had been entertaining Osborne Day, then our senior class officer, at our home in California. Over dinner, some wine and a discussion of the trials of corresponding secretaryship, Oz confided that some years earlier, when he had had my job, he had invented a classmate. I could hardly believe my ears. I pressed him, and although Oz couldn't remember the chap's name, he did remember that he had put him into the Foreign Service and sent him to a U.S. Consulate in some Caribbean republic. Finally, he had thrown the poor fellow into jail (quite unjustly, of course—mistaken identity or something like that), and there the man languished, probably to this day. In one column Oz urged classmates to write their beleaguered classmate and cheer him up.

I refilled Oz's wineglass.

"Oz," I said, "let me tell you about Dave Henderson."

The inventor of a bogus classmate is subject to one omnipresent fear: Discovery. But he has an even greater fear: The possibility that discovery may never occur. He wants to know that at least *one* reader has felt that the events described are not the normal activities of a member of the class of '43.

Thanks to Herb Caen and the *New Yorker,* as querying letters began to pour in from across the country, this latter fear, at least, was allayed.

What could I do but press on? In the December 1988 YAM another Henderson letter appeared:

From Cancún, Mexico, DAVE HENDERSON sends a hurried note: "You can't imagine the damage Hurricane Gilbert inflicted on our spread here! If you can believe it, the winds actually emptied our Olympic-size swimming pool, then the rain filled it halfway-up again! A number of outbuildings—two barns, one of the guest houses, the air-plane hangar—were completely blown away! I am talking to several highly-placed government people in D.F. (Mexico City) about disaster relief. . ."

The next column with word from Dave was for the May 1989 issue. But when the May column appeared in print, Dave's item was not part of it. I sent a note to the Notes Editor: "Sorry my copy ran so long you had to cut it. I assume the unused matter is in the overset, available for my next opus."

No reply.

I queried again and received a cryptic response: "I think the overset might be termed a sleeping dog."

It was then I knew I would have to kill Dave. His time had come. But I wasn't sure quite how to do it. Should he fall overboard from *Triunfador III's* skyscraper bridge? Should he charter the Concorde and choke on a truffle en route to Paris? Should he expire when his stretch limo totals Zsa Zsa Gabor's? Thinking of his high-flying style of life, I finally decided he should die a pedestrian death.

And so I wrote Dave's obituary. I included it in the next column I sent in. A short time later, I phoned the editor and pleaded my case for its publication. He lectured me at some length on the innumerable reasons why he would rather die than run it.

And that is why you are only now learning these tragic facts, as originally conceived and submitted for publication, concerning the untimely death of David Underhill Henderson, Yale, class of 1943:

Closing on a somber note, I have a letter reporting the death of DAVE HENDERSON three weeks before Christmas. From their home in Cancún, Dave's wife Marge writes, "We were about to take Triunfador III through the Canal, and with all the unrest in Panama, Dave thought it would be a wise precaution to arm the crew with assault rifles. He had gone ashore in Belize to try to buy some and was walking back to the boat empty-handed when he was struck down by a speeding pickup truck loaded with mangoes. He died on the way to the hospital..." Dave was buried in a simple family service on the ranch where he was born, now belonging to his brother Richard, near Truth or Consequences, New Mexico. The Class extends its sympathies to Marge and her family.

As I finally came to accept Dave's death, I found I had no feelings of sadness. Dave had had a long and happy life. Six years of that life had been reported extensively in the '43 notes column. In the midst of unlimited corporate success, academic and professional achievement, philanthropy, public service, and happy family life, Dave Henderson had provided a cheerful example of greed, insensitivity, and wretched excess.

What more could a classmate do?

On Beyond Henderson

First, Dave Henderson died under a pickup
loaded with mangoes.
Then, Nadie Doesmith and Nargess Marisal turned up.
And now Bernie Huebner.
How come?

After the story of my bogus classmate Dave Henderson appeared in *Smithsonian*, I began to get letters. Many came from people who were, or had been, class secretaries. The writers represented a variety of schools, and they all had one thing in common. They wanted to confess.

Each had falsified his or her class notes.

Their reasons for sinning were remarkably similar to my own.

Some had buckled under the pressure of an impending deadline and a critical shortage of news.

Others strayed when they realized most of their news came from the same eight or ten classmates upon whom, and upon whose children, great honors were constantly being conferred.

Some wanted to get even for unjust treatment in the past.

Some just wanted to be bad.

So, like me, most of them invented a "URA."

A "URA"?

I am indebted to Heather Killibrew Cowdery for this useful acronym. Heather, at the time of Dave Henderson's death, was Alumni News Editor for the *Dartmouth Alumni Magazine*.

As Heather told me, "URA" means "Unrecorded Alumnus." She was at the time dealing with several URA's, all of whom were appearing, or attempting to appear, in the *Dartmouth Alumni Magazine.* They spanned a cross-section of classes.

The oldest was Alva Edison Adams, from the Dartmouth Class of '41. Alva—Al to his friends, a URA to you—had appeared in the *Alumni Magazine* for many years before Heather got there. Early on, he fought against Franco in Spain. He then joined the Allies. In 1946, he left Allied military service with the rank of Brigadier General. Subsequently, he went trekking in Nepal and elsewhere, returning to the U.S. some time later to rally the peace movement. He earned three post-war degrees, one as a molecular biologist, and contributed to the worldwide elimination of small-pox. He also discovered why the female praying mantis decapi-tates her mate, and developed an antidote for killer bee venom.

Heather entered the *Dartmouth Alumni Magazine* picture shortly before Al and his lovely wife Effie, flying their own plane back from Europe, made a fatal crash landing in the Canary Islands. Heather blew the whistle.

"I had received Mr. Adams' obituary from '41 secretary A. W. 'Monk' Larson," Heather wrote me. "I had got as far as editing it, when it occurred to me there might be a good reason why this guy's life seemed so unbelievable."

"In our magazine the obituaries for all classes appear together in a solemn area separate from the rest of the notes. An obit for an invented '41 classmate, therefore, even one of long standing, would be out of place there. So, much as it pained me, I had to tell Monk it just wouldn't be fair to the families of those alumni who had actually lived before dying to include Alva Adams there. I hope he writes Mr. Adams up in his final column, though."

"The Class of '74 has a couple of URA's," Heather continued. "One is Meg Winthrop. At one time she made a rather spectacular move from a Peace Corps assignment in Bolivia directly to a spot on Oliver North's defense team. Then there was Meg's classmate, Jack Martin, a mystery-writer-criminal-lawyer-stuntman-rodeo-star. Unfortunately, Jack's broken leg put Robert Redford's movie, *The Snows Flow Faster,* on hold. Martin himself puts it this way, 'I have the looks of Robert Redford, the finesse, the romance, and I can ride a horse better than he can.'"

Meg Winthrop and Jack Martin owe their entire existence to Mary Donovan, a real person. Mary writes the notes for her class. Each time she finishes writing a Meg or Jack episode, she reads it to her father. He invariably asks, "Isn't it time to put an end to those two, Mary?"

Mary replies, "Not till they figure it out, Dad."

From Dartmouth we move to a very fine boarding school in Owings Mills, Maryland, the Garrison Forest School. Sylvia Babcock Weaver writes the alumni notes for the Class of 1943.

Strangely enough, the class contains a URA. This URA is one of the many "first name/maiden name/last name" people who appear in the *Garrison Forest Alumni Magazine*, and her name is Nadie Jones Doesmith.

Nadie entered the notes on a slow news day back in 1985. In the magazine Ms. Weaver reported how Nadie had "tumbled out of her basket in a tricky balloon ascension in Baja California."

Nadie's accident resulted in a broken hip, and, like a good Class Secretary, Ms. Weaver wished her a speedy recovery.

Like most URA's, once Nadie had entered the heady world of alumni notes, she was bound to reappear.

Thus, readers of the next issue of the *Garrison Forest Magazine* discovered that Nadie had turned her broken hip to advantage. The '43 class notes column reported that Nadie had won the "Across-Utah Wheelchair Race" in a record time of twenty days, three hours and forty-three minutes. Amazingly, she arrived at the finish line just before midnight on the eve of her sixtieth birthday!

Ms. Weaver's report concluded, appropriately, "Congratulations, Nadie!"

Sometime later, a report from Nadie began, "Although I'm sure no one is interested in the news of a little nobody like myself..." The notes went on to say Nadie had recovered from the broken hip, and was now "sharing a little flat in Brazil with her son Ninguno—'Gooney'—who is taking an extended vacation from the States because of a little trouble with the I.R.S..."

At Kennedy Airport, on the eve of her departure for Brazil, Nadie had sustained a slight concussion from mistakenly entering the 'Exit' door of a Ladies Room. Ms. Weaver reported further, "I'm afraid poor Nad has not entirely recovered, as her handwriting is almost illegible. I could not read her full address..."

Nadie did recover, however, and in time the *Garrison Forest Magazine* carried this reassuring note: "I hear from Nadie Jones Doesmith that she is bravely learning Catalan. She will be skippering a "guest house yacht" in Barcelona during the Summer Olympics, and she wants to be able to deal easily with the local people while taking care of her guests. It is a difficult project, because almost no one around New England is prepared to teach Catalan. And, as Nadie says, she can hardly remember anything anyway, from one day to the next!"

It's a funny thing about URA's. Nobody ever seems to notice them. Dave Henderson lived nearly six years in the pages of the *Yale Alumni News* before anyone took the trouble to look him up in the *Alumni Directory*. For almost as long, the classmates of Nadie Jones Doesmith accepted her as simply another forthright, independent graduate of Garrison Forest.

Farewell, Garrison Forest, hello, College of William & Mary! And hello, Sheila Shiki y Michaels! Sheila is a real person, not a URA. Sheila is definitely not a class secretary. Sheila is a real member of the very real W&M Class of 1959.

You should be warned, therefore, that in the following Class of '59 notes from the October, 1991, *W&M Alumni Magazine,* Sheila's name is the *only* thing real. The note reads as follows:

"Sheila B. Kessler Michaels sent much news of her life. First was the birth of daughter Nargess Marisal. This kept her close to home, because, as she said, 'They like to keep pregnant 50's as close to the hospital as possible.' Meanwhile, she remained busy teaching a theology course on biblical women for the Congregation Beth Simchat Torah."

"Sheila's older children, Duane and SuJeanne, and their live-ins, have been endlessly supportive of the new baby, Sheila says. She hopes the arrival of Nargess has not given them any ideas, however, as Sheila is not yet ready for grandmotherhood!"

"Sheila, her husband LeRoi, and the new baby traveled to Japan last summer where LeRoi collected songs from the Ainu and the Sakhalin Islanders. The autumn in Vostochny reminded Sheila of the overcast rainy winters in Williamsburg, to say nothing of the endless days living in a small town with nothing to do. She commented they were lucky to have permission to be there, though..."

Sheila, the real person, will now explain the presence of all the URA-sounding people in her reports:

"LeRoi appeared in about 1967, when the College of William & Mary asked me what I'd been doing since they'd kicked me out in 1958."

"I didn't want to tell the same people who'd booted me for opposing segregation that I'd spent four years in the South, had become a union organizer and a founder of the women's movement."

"Instead, I invented LeRoi. In the notes I sent to the class secretary I shyly admitted I'd found my perfect mate in him, and we'd had two beautiful lambs. Our babies were such prodigies, you wouldn't believe! Poor LeRoi was struggling to make a living at the Columbia-Princeton Electronic Music Workshop."

"LeRoi was a lamb, too. He was very understanding when I moved in with Ms. Dorothy Dockes and when I announced it to the world through the W&M class notes. And he joined me, without compunction, when, at 48, I announced the birth of my third child, Felicia Garcia-Hernandez. He's a good man, my LeRoi..."

"Later on, in real life, I finally did marry. I decided to report that my Mr. Shiki—his real name—had graduated from Harvard-Yenching, and that we'd been married in Macau in '62. Later, when we met W&M alumni, I never bothered to explain why LeRoi spoke Japanese as a first language. He assured me no one would know the difference, and he was right. They didn't."

"Would that I had married Dave Henderson," Sheila Shiki-y-Michaels wrote. "Not that I would have had a better life than with my own dear LeRoi...but we wouldn't have had to struggle so!"

We move now to Harvard, and Bernie Huebner. Like Sheila Shiki-y-Michaels, Bernie is a real person, not a URA.

However, once every five years, when Bernie reports on his life for the "*Anniversary Report*" of the Harvard Class of 1965, he takes on many URA-like characteristics. In the report for the class's tenth year after graduation, for example, Bernie's listing reads as follows:

"BERNARD HUEBNER: Placekicker/punter; *Quebec Insulaires*. Home, RFD No. 4, No. 138, Skowhegan, Maine 04976. Married: Valerie Olander. Child, Tamarack, July 5, 1972.

"Traveling relentlessly seems to be the basic motif in our otherwise rural existence. I journey four hours each way to spend each weekend in Quebec during the Canadian football season. Valerie, a half-Penobscot Indian, is constantly on the move around the state in connection with her work of treaty evaluation and land restoration for Maine Indians.

"When both of us are away from home, Valerie's sister, Susan Brownflower, stays home with our son in our converted double-silo house in the woods of Somerset County. The structure, which we moved on a drag and rollers from a nearby farm, is the ideal forest home: 360-degree views of game, an intense treetop feeling that plays nicely into all sorts of Tarzan-Jane fantasies, and warm and beautiful inside.

"Crazy as it may seem, Valerie and Tamarack and Susan and I leave this refuge each winter to live with Valerie's other sister and her husband on their fishing boat and in their grass house on the island of Ahe (near Tahiti) in the South Pacific. There, for about two months, we turn Polynesian in all respects save one: Our obsession with the works of Telemann, which we play daily on Valerie's flute and an old French harpsichord left years ago in the village."

Five years later, the *15th Anniversary Report* of Harvard's Class of 1965 carried a further report on Bernie. His address and wife were the same, but Tamarack now had a little brother, Olan. The report continued:

"Having torn up my ankle rather badly by kicking a frozen clod of dirt on the *Insulaires* practice field, I was forced to sit out the entire 1977 Canadian Football League season. As things unfortunately turned out, the front office picked up a replacement kicker and a retired punter, both of whom are still playing for Quebec."

Faced with a complete loss of income, Bernie invested six years of savings from football in a land speculation deal in eastern Maine. When the land grew ten times in value in less than two years, Bernie was tapped to serve on President Carter's *"Commission on Marginal Mineral Investigation and Excavation."*

With their profits, Bernie and Valerie established the first commercially successful lobster farm in the Northeast. The key was the use of a feed composed of processed hardwood pulp, bog peat, and a third mystery ingredient. This enabled the crustaceans to grow to almost two pounds in less than eight months.

"One other interesting development in my life," Bernie's report continues, "grew out of a near disaster. I was inside a local machine shop in 1976 when the building was struck by a rare form of lightning known as St. Elmo's Fire. I was sitting on a lathe just under a large fluorescent fixture when the "fire-balls" came in through the power lines. Doctors estimate the temperature in my brain reached around 108 degrees for a very small fraction of a second.

"The only apparent result of this brief disturbance is what the same doctors are choosing to call, in their articles on the incident, 'enhanced memory'. Incredibly, I can recall at will almost any time in my life after around age two in complete and often sensory detail. Space limits me here, but imagine being able to relive at your leisure your first real Fourth of July fireworks, your first sexual awakenings, the 29-29 Harvard-Yale game!

"Amid all this excitement, I still find great fulfillment in my wife and family and Susan Brownflower, Valerie's sister who is with us less often these days, due to her rising success in state politics. However, while she serves in the bi-cameral legislature in August, we all still live under a uni-cameral system at home."

Bernie's *Twentieth Anniversary Report* found him just back from "Bata, the capital of Quatrain (formerly Rio Muni)..." where, at the request of the Most High Imperial Lord Fanta Katarr, Bernie was making one of his "Custom Memory Prints" of his coronation.

"These Prints", Bernie explains, "are the human cerebral equivalent of a videotape, but with the advantage that I commit to my now absolute memory not only visual images and sounds, but the rich emotional content of an event. My fee—happily of imperial proportions now also—entitles the customer to summon me three times during our joint lifetime for a kind of Homeric rendering of, in this case, the entire coronation. I feel strangely like a genie called forth from a bottle, three wishes in hand.

"The bad news is that my wife is in prison..."

Bernie's *Twenty-Fifth Anniversary Report* was submitted, not by Bernie, but by Bernie's assistant at his business, Hypermnesia, Inc. The reason: Bernie had vanished. The assistant reported:

"Perhaps the last year or so found my employer and long-time friend living more and more within the infinitely detailed Custom Memory Prints he compiled as a professional service for clients worldwide. Last winter, after an unusually heavy season of 'deliveries', as he jokingly called them, I noticed Bernie was beginning to withdraw socially. Finally, late this past spring, he simply vanished..."

"For the record," writes the real Bernie Huebner, "After receiving that first *'Fifth Anniversary Report'* and discovering my fledgling classmates all strutting their tiny feathers in ways that made me want to throw up, I decided to substitute this life for my real one. If I remember correctly back that far, I believe my real aim was to shame at least a few of them into relative silence or at least humility.

"Now, I am in something of a quandary. First, many of my classmates got quite candid and real in the big 25th book, and do not deserve any more to be made fun of. Even more surprising, my own life has taken some hard and crazy turns since my last installment, turns which I now see were somewhat forecast by my writings..."

At this point we'll leave Harvard and return to Yale. Our last URA is an amiable chap named Larry Vaughn.

Larry is from the Yale Class of 1944. I first met him in the pages of *The New Yorker*, where an excerpt from his class notes appeared in tandem with a class note I had written about Dave Henderson. *The New Yorker's* headline for this pair of notes read: *"Department of Life Styles (Old Eli Division)."*

You've already read Dave's note. It's the one in which he said he and Marge had decided, since Marge's father had kicked the bucket the previous year, they could increase the length of their new yacht, still a-building, by 30 or 40 feet. It ended up 197 feet overall.

The report on Larry Vaughn came second hand, from the Secretary of the Class of '44. Here's how it appeared in the *Yale Alumni Magazine.*

"Your Secretary realized an ambition in November when he hiked in Nepal for three weeks, in the stout company of two daughters and a son-in-law. We climbed up to Annapurna Base Camp, with the considerable aid of sherpas and porters. A highlight of the trip was a chance meeting with Larry Vaughn.

"The U.S. Embassy in Kathmandu had advised us, when we checked in, that we might run into an American Buddhist monk named Lawrence Vaughn at the Chonro Monastery at 13,000 feet, the highest populated place on our route. We camped near there late one day and visited the Lamasery. Sure enough, it was our Classmate Larry, and we were permitted to chat with him. He was wearing a maroon homespun cassock and sandals, and his head had been shaved, but by the time we saw him he was just close-cropped.

"He was in fine fettle, and said he is spending two years as a monk there to find himself anew and to meditate on the future. He said he'd gotten out of the market in mid-1987, so he doesn't worry about that. Claudine and their daughter Fleur, now four years old, are staying at the Vaughn's villa in Porto Cervo on Sardinia until Larry finishes his stint in the Himalayas. Claudine flies to Paris every week, where she is taking her doctorate in

Comparative Greek Literature at the Sorbonne. Larry sent his best to all Classmates, and says he'll make the 45th Reunion in June '89 for sure."

Sometimes, late at night, I see a gathering of all these people, URA's and URA-wannabes. It's something like a family picnic. It takes place in the little harbor in Portofino. Larry Vaughn is there with Claudine and Fleur, Bernie Huebner with Valerie and Tamarack and Olan and Susan Brownflower. Meg Winthrop and Jack Martin are there, too, of course, and so are Alva Edison Adams and his lovely wife Effie.

Sheila Shiki-y-Michaels and her beloved LeRoi will show up with Duane, SuJeanne, Felicia Garcia-Hernandez, and Nargess Marisal. Nadie Jones Doesmith will be on hand, perhaps skippering a "guest yacht" where everyone can stay. "Gooney"—Ninguno to you—will mix drinks.

Dave and Marge Henderson, who adore Portofino, will already have been there for a month, living in grand style aboard *Triunfador III*. Their children will be absent, though, since all are currently estranged. Correction: Sondra is not estranged, but since she and Attilo now live in a remote village in Zaire and have three children, they will probably find the journey too taxing.

Naturally, the Hendersons will host this party, a state dinner on board *Triunfador III*, and just as naturally, everyone will be invited. Everyone will show up, everyone will lie extravagantly to everyone else, and everyone will get reasonably drunk.

It will be the greatest URA-party in history. I hope I get invited.

In 1993, the Yale Class of '43 assembled in New Haven for its 50th Reunion. Many Classmates hoped Dave Henderson might attend. Being dead, however, he couldn't make it.

Dave was present in memory, however. Thanks to his appearance in Smithsonian, *Dave had gone from unknown and unnoticed to celebrated and revered. Many drank his health.*

His greatest tribute, however, came during our formal Class Dinner. Several University dignitaries had joined us, and as coffee was passed, President Howard Lamar took the podium.

He thanked us for our substantial reunion gift. He commented on Yale's double duty to our Class during our undergraduate days. The University had not only to educate us, but prepare us for a war most would enter on graduation.

He then spoke of Dave Henderson.

"I know the generations at Yale which came after you will always be in your debt," he said. "I thought that was especially true for your legendary Classmate Dave Henderson, whose exploits I enjoyed so much in the Class Notes section of the Alumni Magazine.*"*

The audience perked up.

"Even though he turned out to be a fictional member of your Class," he concluded, "he is a paradigm nevertheless!"

The audience broke into enthusiastic applause.

The two faces of Dave. The Alumni Magazine *editor hated him, the President of the University loved him. I found a certain satisfaction in that.*

Just before our gathering, the Reunion committee published a Reunion Yearbook. They asked if I would write a word or two in Dave's memory. What follows is my tribute to a man of whom it can truly be said, he was bigger than life.

Henderson's Last Stand

D.U.H., 1921-1989

An Appreciation of
David Underhill Henderson

Fifty Years Out, Published by
Yale University, 1993

The story is common enough. An innocent person—in this case,
a Classmate—is going about his business when, out of nowhere,
Satan appears.

Satan makes the Classmate a mouth-watering proposal. Since
Satan is traditionally strong, and Classmates are traditionally
weak, a deal is struck immediately. And that, ladies and gentlemen, is the story of our late Classmate, Dave Henderson.

I should, however, point out one thing. It wasn't Dave to whom
Satan appeared. It was to me.

The time was 1984. I was writing the *1943 Class Notes* for
the *Yale Alumni Magazine*. Since our Class suffers from chronic,
if not terminal, writer's cramp, I was in trouble: I had nothing
to report. The few scraps I had—company news releases about
Classmates being named C.E.O. or Executive Vice President, or
being appointed to the boards of mighty corporations—made my
problem even worse: I was not only short of news, I was having
trouble staying awake!

That's when Satan appeared. He was a better-looking guy than I would have expected. Chiseled features, $1,500 suit, hand-made shoes, nice, warm smile. He perched on the corner of my desk and asked a question.

"How would you like never to have trouble filling that lousy column again?"

The idea was ludicrous. "Yeah?" I said. "How?"

"I'll give you a brand new Classmate to write about," Satan said. "Dave Henderson. You'll love him—he's got no morals whatever! He's rich, his kids hate him, he looted his company in New York, and now he's living it up on a big spread in Cancún. He's even bought himself a deal with the Mexican government so he's extradition-proof! Whaddya think of that?"

"Get real!" I said. "He may be colorful, but he'd never let me print that kind of stuff!"

"Hell," Satan said, pronouncing the word reverently, "this guy Henderson would love it! He talks about it to everyone! He'll make great copy! *And*," he added, lifting his thick eyebrows, "he doesn't have writer's cramp. He'll send you more stuff than you can possibly print!"

A sudden thought came to me. "Hey," I said, "What do *you* get out of this?"

"Only your soul," Satan said. "Such as it is."

The rest is history. Satan kept his word—he usually does—and for the next six years Dave Henderson kept the mail coming, in quantity, from Cancún, from London, and from his yachts *Triunfador II* and *Triunfador III*. During that magical period, our Class Notes never ran short.

Smithsonian Magazine, bless its heart, in its March, 1991, issue, reprinted many of Dave's communications to the *'43 Notes* column, including Dave's very first postcard, which I would like to reprise here:

Writing from his winter home in Cancún, DAVE HENDER-SON reports that his company finally lost its long bout with chapter eleven. Says Dave philosophically, "I didn't really mind—I was sick and tired of trying to breathe life into the damned thing!" Dave says he had several pleasant conversations with two Class members he met at the Betty Ford Clinic last fall..."

Those who read about Dave in *Smithsonian* might like to read a few of his letters that were *not* included in that article. They all appeared in our *Notes* column, however, back in those golden days before the Dave Henderson situation hit the *Alumni Magazine* fan. When that happened, of course, I was forced to—well, to kill Dave. In my defense, let me point out that, despite considerable provocation, Dave is the only Classmate I have killed to date.

To set the stage for Dave's *Notes*, there are a couple of things you should know. First, unlike the rest of our Class, Dave and his lovely wife Marge were frequently at odds with their children. The one exception was their daughter Sondra. In 1985, when the terms of Sondra's parole could not be modified sufficiently to permit her to spend Easter at the Cancún spread, Dave and Marge flew to New York to spend it with her at the Plaza.

With the other children, however, there were frequent problems. From the March '87 *Notes*:

"Marge finally talked me into reconciling with our born-again daughter Pamela and her husband Hobart. As a result, they brought their five kids to visit us in Mexico for two weeks over Christmas—the first time they had seen our spread in Cancún, and even more important, the first time we had ever seen our grandchildren. Now, thank God, they have returned to North Dakota. We love Pamela a great deal, of course, and Marge and I both feel the grandkids could be real winners if we could have them here alone for awhile. It's a real pain, however, to have them whisper to their parents about every damn thing Marge and I eat, drink, read, say, or do..."

It took Dave Junior, however, to break his father's heart. Dave's cry of pain appeared in our May, 1987, *Notes:*

"I wonder if anyone in the Class has had the extreme annoyance and indignity of being sued by one's own child. Five years ago I would never have believed it possible for Dave Junior to sue Marge and me for anything, least of all for 'child neglect, in that defendants failed to provide appropriate role models during plaintiff's childhood; further, defendants failed to instill in plaintiff adequate respect for the law; further, defendants failed to provide the discipline necessary to enable plaintiff to establish and maintain effective, on-going, interpersonal relationships.' What utter garbage! He's got a big New York law firm in on it, so it's not just fun and games. As we see it, the whole thing is a ploy to get us to keep him from going public. The way we do this, of course, is by making a big, out-of-court settlement. I'm so damned mad, though, and so is Marge, that we've decided if the kid wants to play hardball, we'll give him lessons! Fortunately, living in Mexico provides some initial insulation. Most of the legal fraternity here, and all of the judiciary, would consider a son who tried to sue padre y madre *not only a fool but a traitor! Then there's the fact that most of the assets Dave Junior would love to attach are not that easily found. Still, if anyone in the Class has experience with this kind of thing, I hope they'll get in touch..."*

Did *you* respond to Dave's call for help? No, of course you didn't! Neither did anyone else in '43! Fortunately, a compassionate member of the Class of 1948 sent the following to Dave, via me, with a cover note reading: *"Please forward the enclosed letter to Dave Henderson at his address in Cancún, Mexico."*

"Dear Mr. Henderson:

"Since 1956 I have been practicing law in New Haven. During that period I was solicited by several thankless children like your son. I threw them, one and all, out of my office.

"You are right about the pleadings of your son's lawyers— utter garbage. They should be disbarred for making such allegations. Such claims should never be given credence in any degree. Therefore, you must refuse to settle for any amount whatsoever. If you do settle, you will lose my respect. If you can live without my respect, try living without your own self-respect.

"If this matter were in Connecticut, I would handle your side of the case as a public service for no fee.

"Very truly yours,

"Robert C. Ruggiero"

When I sent thanks to Mr. Ruggiero on Dave's behalf, and explained my deal with Satan, he replied:

"Your letter has restored my faith in Dave. When he did not reply, I assumed he had knuckled under to his son's lawyers. It is now your duty to see his name never dies..."

Dave Henderson appeared in our Class *Notes* 15 times. On occasion, he cruised the South American coast in his yacht, *Triunfador II*. Once, he was arrested in S. João do Monte for "alleged trafficking in illegal substances." Once, with Marge, he visited Lourdes, seeking a cure for Marge's painful tennis elbow.

When his daughter Sondra's parole ended, she married Attilo

Katakunle, number three man in Zaire's Ministry of Tourism. Then, in early '86, Imelda Marcos visited the Henderson *estancia* in Cancún, bringing her cook, her bodyguard, and her hairdresser. Late in 86, *Triunfador II* was sent to the bottom by pirates who boarded her in the Malacca Straits. In early '87, in Kobe, Japan, a keel was laid for *Triunfador III*. The boat finally came down the ways in January, 1988, amid a gala celebration to which every member of '43 within hailing distance was invited.

Without doubt, Dave was the most hospitable member of our Class. His invitations were numerous and permanent. If a Class-mate spotted *Triunfador III* in any harbor on the globe, he was invited to come aboard for a drink and "some of Andre's gourmet chow." As for *Cobayos de Oro*, Dave's palatial home in Cancún, his Classmates, their wives, their families, were all welcome to visit for a day, a week, or as long they chose.

On May 2, 1988, a day that will live in infamy, someone blew the whistle on Dave Henderson. In Herb Caen's column in *The San Francisco Chronicle* a note of Dave's appeared, reprinted from the *Y.A.M.* Shortly thereafter, that same note appeared in *The New Yorker* under, *"Department of Life Styles, (Old Eli Division)."* It read:

"I have a long letter from DAVE HENDERSON, with pictures of the launching of his new boat, Triunfador III. *Says Dave, 'Our shiny new putt-putt was to have been 163 feet overall, but after Marge's father kicked the bucket last year, we figured we could go another 30-40 feet. So, we re-did the whole plan, and now it's 197 feet stem-to-stern, fitted out with every electronic marvel known to man, and furnished like a Sultan's harem! I feel like a kid with a new toy, and so does Marge! The other day she walked into the owner's suite—the whole thing's done in white-on-white—collapsed on the bed, and began to cry, she was so happy! Incidentally, we've got a new chef on board, and we're heading for*

Italy and the Côte d'Azur *in May. Any '43-ers who spot us in one of the harbors in that neighborhood are invited for drinks and some of Andre's gourmet chow...!'"*

In San Francisco, a concerned Yale graduate clipped Dave's note from the *Chronicle* and sent it to then-President Benno Schmidt. He commented on the Hendersons' poor taste in add-ing—as a direct result of Marge's father's demise—34 feet to *Triunfador III's* hull. He noted that John Quinn, Catholic Arch-bishop of San Francisco, and Episcopal Bishop William Swing had both censured the Hendersons—by deed, not by name—one from the pulpit, the other across the luncheon table. The concerned graduate's name was John Faux.

President Schmidt responded promptly.

"Dear Mr. Faux:

"I agree that the quotation about benefiting from the death of another is in bad taste. It may well be that Mr. Hender-son never intended his comment to be printed in the Class Notes, let alone in The San Francisco Chronicle. *I suggest you write directly to the Secretary of the Class of 1943 to express your concern.*

"Sincerely,

"Benno C. Schmidt, Jr."

I smelled a double-agent. An alumnus named Faux? A John Faux claiming concern about our *faux* Classmate? But I was wrong. Mr. Faux—pronounced, incidentally, "Fox"—turned out to be a member of the Class of 1940, and was broad-minded enough to laugh when I revealed Satan's bargain.

In May '88, the *Notes* announced Dave's schedule for a series of dockside dinners aboard *Triunfador III*. All Class members living in New York, New Jersey, and Connecticut were invited. Alas, as this October, '88, *Note* explains, these dinners were not to take place.

> *"Regret we had to remove New York from* Triunfador III's *1988 itinerary, thereby postponing our proposed series of Class-dinners-on-board. We'll do it next summer for sure. Meanwhile, you might be interested to know that when we took* Triunfador *into Stockholm this past summer and headed for a choice berth alongside the main pier—a berth I had reserved months before—we found it already occupied by Donald Trump's new 300-foot monster,* Trump Princess! *I took my confirming documentation ashore and pounded my fist bloody on the Harbormaster's desk, but it was no dice—I suspect quite a lot of money had already changed hands to get us pre-empted!* Trump Princess *is absolutely beyond belief! As Marge says, it's so big, it's grotesque! Neither one of us can understand how anyone could buy something so lacking in taste!"*

In December of 1988, Dave reported extensive damage to his Cancún spread, caused by Hurricane Gilbert. Tragically, several outbuildings—two barns, one of the guest houses, the airplane hangar—were all blown away.

It was Dave's last appearance in the *Notes*. For the May, '89 issue I sent in Dave's account of his trip to Zaire to visit two new grandchildren. It didn't appear in print. I suspected the *Chronicle* and *New Yorker* items had blown Dave's cover. I resubmitted my report of Dave's trip. It still didn't appear.

I phoned the *Alumni Magazine* and spoke to the Editor. He made it clear he would quite cheerfully drink hemlock rather than permit Dave, or Marge, or their children, or their goods and chattels, or their spread in Cancún, or their limousines and yachts, to darken the pages of the *Yale Alumni Magazine* again.

So, I killed Dave.

I will spare you his obituary. It told of his death in Belize, under the wheels of a pickup truck loaded with mangoes. He was returning to *Triunfador III* from a fruitless search for assault rifles. Rejected by the *Y.A.M.*, it appeared—handsomely illustrated—in *Smithsonian*. Dave would have liked that.

I began receiving sympathy cards. One read, *"Was sorry to learn of the passing of Dave Henderson, poor devil."* Another said, *"We are, of course, shocked and saddened to hear of his last journey to the place where all will go, and none, save perhaps one, has ever returned. He will be missed..."*

Shortly thereafter, the notice heralding the Annual '43 Cherry Blossom Dinner in Washington, D.C. noted that the ceremonies would include *"a solemn moment of silence in memory of Dave Henderson"*.

And yet...and yet... Was Dave really dead? Was he a fiction? Was he, too, a deal done with Satan? I received many letters from Classmates who suggested otherwise.

Oz Day wrote:

"I remember Henderson well. He was a mousy little guy. I think at one time he was assistant manager of the Berkeley fencing team..."

Don Marsden remembered Dave Henderson. He wrote:

"...he was a tall, bespectacled guy who used to play in pick-up basketball games at the gym..."

Don wrote again a few months later, saying,

"Sometime this summer I awoke to realize I was thinking of Charlie Frankenhoff. He doesn't sound much like Dave Henderson. Our 25th Yearbook shows him as a priest teaching economics in Puerto Rico..."

Responding to a note from a mutual friend, Dick Ketchum wrote,

"Sure, I know Jim Nelson. He was in my class. What you probably don't know is that I also knew Dave Henderson. He was in my class, and, unless I'm mistaken, in my fraternity..."

From the Class of 1944, Circuit Judge Jim Buckley of the U.S. Court of Appeals wrote:

"Frankly, I was surprised that you were taken in by Marge's disinformation. She and Dave were simply fed up with all the ridicule and hate mail generated by Caen and The New Yorker, *and thought this was the best way to liberate themselves—especially as no members of your class had ever accepted their invitation to visit them on* Triunfador III! *Too bad, because it is a magnificent boat—or at least was as of last October when I visited with Dave and Marge off Tangier..."*

Quite recently, another Classmate wrote:

"Dear Jim,

"I have read only recently your report of the sad death of our Classmate Dave Henderson. His career, which I have followed with wonder in the Y.A.M., seemed a bit startling at first, because when I knew him, he didn't have two cents to bless himself with. He was a waiter with me in the Graduate School dining room, to which I had been banished after I had dumped a full tray of dishes in Commons.

"So, when I read of his remarkable adventures in Cancún and elsewhere, I realized that, no matter how humble our

origins, we bursary students often had the potential for greatness.

"I am shocked, however, at the doubts expressed about Dave's genuineness. I can see his face now as if it were yesterday—oval, a bit soft, an O-shaped mouth and heavy-lidded eyes. He had a slightly splay-footed stride, and—oh, he was there, all right, and even if the Alumni Office has lost his record, I, at least, have not forgotten him!

"I truly regret that the outrageous puritanical prejudice and political pressure of the "administration" has brain-washed even you, James Nelson, into believing that you had actually invented Dave Henderson, and then treacherously killed him. My personal opinion is that he not only lives, but that he will rise again to entertain us. In anticipation of that desired event, I pardon your momentary (and wholly forgivable) lapse from strict truth.

"Sincerely,

"Hal Melcher"

Naturally, I was forced to reply.

"Dear Hal,

"Interestingly enough, in the many ship-to-shore phonecalls I receive from Dave Henderson, he often speaks of you. In one conversation he said his days in the Graduate School dining room were the happiest of his life. Coming to Yale from Truth or Consequences, New Mexico, he had very little idea of how to comport himself in the rarefied Eastern atmosphere. You, he said, provided him with a role model.

He attributed a great deal of his success in arbitrage, junk bonds, and the stripping of assets from merged companies, to your early influence.

"Only recently, Dave said his Grad School dining room days gave him a sense of freedom—albeit with a strong admixture of servitude—that never left him. His comradeship with you and the other waiters enriched his life in ways he never dreamt of back in the harsh, New Mexican landscape. It provided him a series of little epiphanies that, unfortunately, never reoccurred once he became rich, famous, and, if we're going to be completely honest, infamous.

"You can understand, therefore, Hal, how pleased I was to receive your letter. It gives me the opportunity to reveal to you, in the strictest confidence, the fact that you are right: Dave is indeed living at this moment. Under the much-maligned Witness Protection Program (maligned unfairly, I might add!) Dave and Marge live on another continent, one you would recognize instantly if I were to give you the smallest of hints. I will tell you only that Spanish and Portuguese are the principal languages spoken on this continent, and let you take it from there.

"If Dave were to come to our Fiftieth…oh, the tales he could tell! Not just about the past—Ollie North and Reagan and Casey and all that old stuff—but of Milken and Noriega and B.C.C.I. and Escobar and God-knows-what! Alas, we will not see him there.

"Guess that's it, Hal. Incidentally, I noted that your return letterhead says 'Wilton, New Hampshire'. Actually, Wilton is in Connecticut, and you may want to make the change before you confuse someone. In the meantime, I will cer-

tainly tell Dave, in my next shadow contact through his safe-house-computer-mail-drop, of your continuing interest in his welfare.

"Sincerely,

"Jim Nelson"

In early 2003, "The Ten Greatest Yalies Who Never Were*" appeared in the* Yale Alumni Magazine.

The cover featured Mike Doonesbury, Garry Trudeau's cartoon icon who made his debut in the Yale Daily News *of the late 1960s. Inside the magazine, Mike was joined by Tom Buchanan from F. Scott Fitzgerald's* Great Gatsby, *Sherman McCoy from Tom Wolfe's* Bonfire of the Vanities, *TV villain C. Montgomery Burns from* The Simpsons, *and six other distinguished, if totally fictional, Yalies.*

Imagine Dave Henderson's pleasure at being one of them!

Later in the year the Class of 1943 held its 60th Reunion. I got a call. Was Dave alive? Would I report on him?

I wrote the letter that follows to record Dave's most recent exploits. I sent it off to New Haven, and my classmate Osborne Day read it at the Class Dinner.

Henderson Redux

Dear Oz,

You're a good guy to present my Dave Henderson report to the Class. Thanks a lot.

Naturally, Mary-Armour and I wish we could be there. We send our warmest greetings to everyone—Classmates, wives, widows, companions, offspring.

So...what about Dave?

Some Classmates still think Dave died down in Belize, that he was run over by a pickup truck loaded with mangoes. Those who've paid attention know that was a C.I.A. cover story.

So, Dave and Marge are both still alive...and well...and still in the Witness Protection Program.

Where do they live? I'll give you a tiny hint. This is confidential and must not leave this room: Dave and Marge live in a country where Portuguese is spoken.

Not by Dave, of course.

Dave has a young Portuguese-speaking couple who also speak English living on his finca. They interpret for him, and for Marge, whenever it's necessary to talk to the locals.

You might think people in the Witness Protection Program couldn't communicate with friends, but Dave has found a way. He sends his messages through a convoluted e-mail system that's nominally operated by the Department of Homeland Security. Actually, it's run by the W.P.P., or as Dave likes to call them, "The Witnesses."

Dave says, except for having to live under an assumed name, he's happier than he's ever been. Here's an e-mail he sent last December:

> "...When I think how I used to get persecuted by the damned IRS and the damned SEC and OSHA and the damned EPA, the life I lead now is a dream. It has a few tiny drawbacks, but listen to this: My ulcers are completely gone, have been for six years, and my blood pressure is down to 185 over 99..."

> "...Besides, when we went into this Program, the deal we cut with the Witnesses let us keep our dear boat Triunfador III. All we had to do was paint it in camouflage colors and get rid of the helicopter..."

> "...This means Marge and I still spend three or four months each year in the Mediterranean. We love to hang out in Portofino. Other times, we have the crew take the boat out to Southeast Asia or the east coast of Africa. Then we fly over and join it..."

> "...Here's the best news: A couple of years ago we found a way to make the Witnesses pay the boat upkeep! How about that? It means you're paying for us to keep our boat, old buddy, isn't that a kick...?"

I e-mailed Dave back, asking him how Mary-Armour and I could get into the Witness Protection Program. He didn't reply. In February of this year, however, he sent another message:

"...Do you remember my daughter Pamela and her husband Hobart? They lived up in North Dakota, had five kids... belonged to some cockamamie religious sect that all lived like hermits..."

"...Well, when Marge and I realized this Witness Protection thing meant we couldn't live on our Cancún spread any more, guess what happened?..."

"...Guess who now is living in 54 rooms with two tennis courts and an Olympic swimming pool? And three guest houses, and an air strip...?"

"...Well, it's good old Pammie and Hobie! They asked if they could move in, and since none of our other kids wanted to live in Cancún, we said okay..."

"...They were there in a week! Talk about deprogramming! What's more, even though you wouldn't expect it, they give parties like you wouldn't believe...!"

"...Incidentally, Jim, I hope you will pass this message along for Marge and me: If any member of the Class of '43...ever...wants to spend a night, or a weekend...or hell, a couple of weeks...in Cancún...a call to Pamela will set it up in a New York minute..."

"...Just mention my name. Tell her you're from '43. They'd love to have you...!"

Dave said he'd e-mail me their phone number. When I get it, I'll pass it on to Bob Lincoln for the Class Notes.

I got this last e-mail from Dave just a few weeks ago:

"...Jim: Would you pass this along to Lincoln for me?"

"...First off, Dave Junior and I buried the hatchet a few years ago. You remember he sued Marge and me for not being good role models when he was growing up..."

"...Well, he lost his case, of course, and after awhile we both decided, what the hell, let bygones be bygones. Now he's a middle-aged guy with a son of his own, and his son just came back from Iraq..."

"...Dave Junior named the kid Dave Henderson the Third, which has kind of a nice ring to it.

"...At first I didn't think the kid was too bright, so I tried to help him with some advice. I told him a lot of stuff, but one thing I made a big point about was, stay clear of the military, there's no money in it..."

"...He listened to me, but you know kids! I guess he thought he'd look good in a uniform. Anyhow, he up and joined some National Guard outfit, and next thing you know he's on his way to Kuwait, and next thing after that he's marching to Baghdad..."

"...Well, he's not actually marching. They don't march any more. He's riding in some personnel carrier. Anyhow, when he gets to Baghdad there's a lot of noise and shooting, and in all the confusion someone beans him with a brick or a bottle or something..."

"...A day or two later the kid wakes up, he's Looney Tunes, he's wandering around Baghdad like he's on vacation..."

"...And then some medic spots him, and before he knows it they've put a humongous bandage on his head, and he's flying home on a stretcher with a duffle bag full of souvenirs under his bunk..."

"...Now he's home, and he's got a nice picture of Saddam's niece painted on black silk right over his bureau, very pretty. And he's got some kind of automatic pistol that Iraqi officers carry..."

"...And he's also got this big chunk of what looks like, well, I guess you'd call it a wall sculpture..."

"...It's mostly made out of ebony, with some silver and some ivory worked in. It's real old, and it's got these two big bulls facing each other on the front, just the heads, not the whole bull, done in some metal that sort of looks like gold. Hell, maybe it is gold, who am I to say...?"

"...Anyhow, Dave the Third doesn't like me to talk about this stuff. It makes him uncomfortable..."

"...I tell him as long as I don't talk in Portuguese—which is not about to happen—nobody down here is going to know diddly about it anyhow..."

"...Well, he's a great kid, Jim. And you know...when I think about him...ignoring his grandfather's advice... joining up anyhow...and then coming home flat on his ass with all that stuff...well, I don't want to go all mushy on you, but it makes me kind of proud..."

Well, Oz, that's the most recent e-mail I have from Dave. Thanks for helping pass his words along to the Class.

I know Dave appreciates it. And I know that wherever he and Marge are tonight, they'd much rather be here, inviting everyone in this room to come on down to the New Haven Harbor after dinner.

When we'd get there, that great 197-foot yacht, Triunfador III, would be tied up at the dock. And Dave and Marge would be standing at the gangway, welcoming everyone aboard for after-dinner drinks...and for a lot of talk about all those Bright College Years.

Best regards, Oz...

Jim

Part Two: Etc...

Willis Kingsley Wing
1899-1985

Willis Kingsley Wing

In 85 years I've written a lot of stuff. Short stories, ads, books, speeches, articles for newspapers and magazines. It occurred to me recently that I'd written a lot of it before our four children were old enough to read. Some before the last was even born.

For them, therefore, I decided to gather a few of my favorite pieces and put them into a book. As I dug the material out of file cabinets and started reading it, however, I began to realize who I was really doing this for.

Me.

It's unseemly to admit how much fun it is to read your own stuff. Partly, it's the writing itself, and partly it's remembering where and when you wrote it, and under what circumstances. I wrote five of the stories in this book in a converted dog kennel. It sat behind the ranch foreman's house on what had once been the Spreckels estate in Sonoma County, California. In the early Fifties, Sonoma had not yet been "discovered." Mary-Armour and I rented this architect-remodeled, four-bedroom house, set in the middle of forty lush acres of farmland, for a pathetically small amount of money.

The dog kennel was my office. My desk, a slab door mounted on cinder blocks, held my portable typewriter, a ream or two of blank paper, and my files—a stack of stories, each sheltered in its manila folder. Outside, our kids played on the broad, sloping lawn, or rode wheel toys on the paved driveway that led from the latched gate to the garage.

From time to time Mary-Armour would bring me a freshly baked cookie, or a glass of iced tea. Or, if I were terribly lucky, both.

It was truly paradise. We lived in the beautiful Valley of the Moon. Living didn't cost much. I was freelancing, something I had always wanted to do. And, the money hadn't run out. Yet.

The 1950's were a wonderful time for would-be short story writers. Television was in its infancy. Sitcoms and soap operas had yet to be invented. How did people fill the vast amount of time they now spend watching television? They read. They read books, they read newspapers, they read cereal boxes, and, lucky for short story writers, they also read magazines.

The Saturday Evening Post was the most desirable market for short fiction. For one thing, it paid most. For another, selling a story to *The Post* was akin to being canonized. *Collier's* and half a dozen women's magazines were not far behind *The Post*. They all carried two or three short stories per issue, and the amounts they paid, though slightly less than *The Post*, seemed staggering to writers who had yet to make their first sale.

Midway through 1955, therefore, with high hopes and a stamped, self-addressed envelope, I sent *The Saturday Evening Post* a story titled, *Mr. Meigs*. I allowed them three weeks to read it and get back to me. After this time elapsed, I began a daily series of late-morning walks from the dog kennel to our mailbox on the county road. Each day I opened the box and reached in to find *The Post's* flattering letter of acceptance and its handsome check.

After an agonizing wait, something did finally arrive from *The Post*. It was my manuscript. There was no letter. There was no check. There was, however, a rejection slip. In cold, black type it thanked me for sending my story. It then told me of the magazine's enormous short story backlog. Finally, it told me how, to its great regret, this backlog limited the magazine's ability to buy new stories. Mine, for instance.

The manuscript was a bit dog-eared from its exciting trip to Philadelphia. Being jammed into our mailbox hadn't helped, either. I showed it to Mary-Armour.

"I'm going to have to retype the whole damn thing," I said.

Mary-Armour examined the manuscript. She got out the ironing board and plugged in the iron.

"What are you doing?" I asked.

"I'm going to iron it," she said.

Page by page she pressed my manuscript. When she finished, the manuscript looked as though it had just come from the typewriter.

I wrote a new cover letter and sent *Mr. Meigs* off to *Ladies Home Journal*. A couple of months later it came back. The rejection slip deplored the fact that my story, though admirable, did not match the exacting criteria for the type of story they were seeking at the moment.

The manuscript didn't need ironing this time, but the starch had gone out of the writer. I decided I would lay this story aside for the moment. It was obvious *Mr. Meigs* wasn't the kind of story editors wanted to buy at this particular moment in history. Instead, I would send out the much better story I had just finished. I would keep on writing. I would try to sell other pieces. Later, maybe, I would give *Mr. Meigs* another shot or two.

The next story I sent out suffered the same indignity. So did the story after that. There was never a letter from a kindly editor, never a check from a generous accounting department. There was just the same, smarmy, insincere, and—worst of all—*printed*, rejection slip. The stories went out, the stories came back. Mary-Armour ironed them. End of story.

But, wait! That's not the end after all! Fortunately, at this time I was also trying to sell a book about our adventures coming west from New York. On landing in California we'd bought a route of penny gum machines to provide income until I became a famous writer. We'd spent an inordinate amount of time and energy trying to make the route profitable, but alas, it had not provided the hoped-for riches. It had, however, provided raw material for a book. I called the book *The Adventures of Captain Gumball.*

I'd sent the book to *Simon & Schuster,* and had received a wonderfully prompt and cheering letter from an editor named Jack Strauss.

Jack liked my book, but felt it needed some reworking. He also said I needed an agent. Best of all, he offered to put me in touch with one.

This is how I met—by mail—Willis Kingsley Wing. Willis was a top New York agent and a true gentleman. He asked me to send him a few stories. He read them, then wrote back he'd be happy to represent me.

There were many nice things about having Willis as my agent. The nicest, perhaps, was that Willis didn't feel wounded when a magazine declined to buy one of my stories. If Willis liked a story, he'd send it by messenger to every last fiction editor in New York. If that didn't produce a sale, he'd send it to a long list of out of town editors. To him, my story, however fine, was just merchandise. It would sell, or it wouldn't sell. There was no place for hurt feelings.

Willis took my twice-rejected manuscript of *Mr. Meigs* and put it on the road again It went out, it came back, it went out, it came back. Willis kept me abreast of what was happening. Sometimes he sent me the editor's letter that had accompanied the returned piece, especially if it contained some helpful comment. On *Mr. Meigs'* fourteenth time out—Willis was indefatigable—a Canadian magazine named *Chatelaine* bought it. I had never heard of *Chatelaine*, and I felt the sale was a miracle. But it was not a miracle. It was a lesson in perseverance—Willis's perseverance.

Chatelaine politely asked—through Willis—if they might re-title my story *The Trouble With Ada.* I fell all over myself saying yes, yes, yes!

Before he was through, Willis sold *The Trouble With Ada* to Belgian, Dutch, and Danish magazines, and to *Homemaker*, an Australian magazine that had the poor taste to go out of business before they could publish it.

Chatelaine paid $400 for the privilege of running my story. In 1956, $400 was a king's ransom! This fact, incidentally, is something you should keep in mind when you encounter money figures in *The Trouble With Ada,* which follows, and which marks my entry into paid fiction writing.

The Trouble With Ada

Chatelaine, (Canada) October, 1956

Mr. Meigs celebrated his seventy-fourth birthday alone in his wallboard-finished attic room, because his son, who might have remembered had he been home, was in Ottawa on business, and his daughter-in-law, Ada, who was left nominally in charge of the old man, was far too busy with her clubs and committees and charity drives to recall a date of such small consequence.

"Father Meigs," Ada had said to him that morning, as she tried to hurry him through his breakfast so she could tidy up and be off, "I'll be away most of the day working with the symphony committee. I've put your lunch in the refrigerator, so all you have to do is warm it up. Are you through with your coffee?"

Mr. Meigs gulped the remainder of his coffee.

"Yes, thanks," he said. He rose from his chair and carried the cup, rattling ever so slightly in its saucer, to the sink.

"Don't let me rush you."

Even as she said it, Ada realized she only half meant it. There was so much to be done today. On days like this, Father Meigs was just another of her projects. A special project, to be sure, since he was John's father and a good old soul. But still a project, a cause to be shepherded and guided and managed as efficiently as next month's old clothes drive.

Not that she wasn't fond of the slow, fumbling, old gentleman. Of course she was. He often made her laugh with his gentle reminiscences, and she was touched by his occasional invitations to dinner while John was away. But still there was no doubt he was becoming more of a problem every day. In fact, it was her private opinion—she never discussed it with anyone but John, of course—but it was her opinion that the man had been failing ever since the day two years ago when, at John's insistence, he had given up his furnished front room on West Fourth street and moved in with them.

Mr. Meigs lived on the second floor, which contained, besides his room, a small bathroom and a great deal of unfinished attic. Although Ada, because of her many civic projects, had little time to clean or otherwise tend to Mr. Meigs's tiny room, she did try to inspect it once or twice a week to make sure the old man remembered to change his sheets and towels and sweep his tobacco crumbs off the splintery floor. At these times she occasionally wondered if her father-in-law would ever learn to make his bed with hospital corners. She'd shown him how enough times, and how to turn the counterpane back, just so, the way she did her bed and John's.

She watched the old man turn from the sink and look toward her. She already had her smart, yellow hat on, as a sort of notice that, except for cleaning up after him, she was ready to go.

"I'll do the dishes, Ada," Mr. Meigs said, "and empty the scrap baskets, and…"

"No, no," Ada said, half bantering. half impatient. "Our dish supply can't stand many more of your dishwashings."

"I know," the old man said apologetically. "I'm trying to find where I can buy your pattern."

Mr. Meigs turned to the counter beside the sink where the garbage bag lay. He put one careful hand on either side of the bag, picked it up, and turned cheerfully toward the back door.

"Well, at least I can take out the garbage," he said.

It was not a mistake he made often, and he realized, just a split second too late, that it was going to happen.

"Look out!" Ada called, as the soggy bottom burst out of the garbage bag and splattered the contents of the sack onto the red-and-black linoleum.

"Oh dear!" Mr. Meigs said, looking down at the flattened heap of garbage. "I'm terribly sorry, Ada!"

Ada Meigs sucked in her breath and shut her eyes.

"Honestly!" she said.

The old man got down on one knee and began to gather the pile together with his hands.

"You go on," he said. "I'll clean it up. I did it."

"You did it, all right!" Ada said. She walked swiftly toward the old man. "No, let me," she said. "You'll just find some way to make it worse."

"No, I won't, Ada. I'll just..."

"Go fiddle with your stamps!" Ada said. "Or take a walk, or do something! Please leave the kitchen to me!"

"Well, I'd like to help," Mr. Meigs said slowly. "Isn't there something for me to do?"

"There's plenty to do," Ada said crisply, looking at her tiny wrist watch, "but I doubt if you could do it!"

Mr. Meigs, with the implication clearly before him that he was too old and doddering to be of use to anyone, climbed slowly up the unpainted, unrailed stairs to his room. Shaking his white head slowly, he sat down on the straight chair lent reluctantly from the kitchen (it made the kitchen one chair short when John was home, which was not too often) and leaned his elbow on the unpainted pine table.

Oh well, Ada meant no harm. He knew that. She just had a lot to do, that was all. Mr. Meigs knew that an old man is a lot of trouble around the house. And he knew, too, that he was lucky to have a son who wanted to take him in and look after him. Still, no one liked to be thought of as a burden or reminded constantly of his uselessness.

Mr. Meigs shrugged. Thank heaven he had his stamps!

He pulled his chair closer to the table and opened the latest envelope of stamps sent on approval by one of the big mail-order stamp houses. He pulled his well-thumbed catalogue into easy reach and picked up his magnifying glass. He was now ready to embark on his exciting daily journey through the varicolored stamps of countless foreign countries, all endlessly exotic and far away from the world of wallboard rooms and garbage bags.

Sometimes Mr. Meigs became so absorbed in his stamp travels that he forgot lunch. Ordinarily, when Ada was home, lunch was served promptly at twelve o'clock. Ada never summoned Mr. Meigs to this meal, expecting him rather to keep an eye on the clock and save her the trouble and the time. Time, Mr. Meigs knew, was terribly important to anyone as busy as Ada. Finally, on these days, when at twelve-thirty or one o'clock his stomach called him back gently from Portugal or China or Afghanistan, he would totter down the steep stairway and out into the empty kitchen to find Ada gone, and his lunch sitting on the table, soup cold as ice, yesterday's meat loaf which had been briefly warm at noon now frigid, his coffee even colder.

"I thought you might be sleeping," Ada had told him once, when in his most apologetic tone he'd mentioned not being called. He told her he never napped during the morning unless he had one of his colds, but just then the telephone rang, and Mr. Meigs guessed the whole thing had slipped Ada's mind.

After all, it was probably his own fault if Ada was a trifle short with him now and then, and...well, it was still worth it to be with his son during the few brief days he was home between trips. He couldn't really blame Ada, who had married John in a ceremony that mentioned love, honor, and obedience, but had made no mention whatever of caring for doddering old fools like himself. It was an imposition, and he knew it, but what else could an old man do, with only an old-age pension of forty dollars a month, and a few hundred dollars in the bank.

As Mr. Meigs focused his magnifying glass on the first stamp, he had a fleeting, troubled vision. He seemed to see the years ahead of him (how many?) stretching out like a narrow, threadbare carpet laid across a vast swamp. And he realized suddenly that without the brief visits from John—and his stamps—he would long ago have been swallowed up in the bog.

Mr. Meigs had a headache when Ada arrived home that night. She stood in the entrance to the living room and fixed him with a shrewd stare.

"You have another headache, don't you?" Ada said flatly.

Mr. Meigs laid down the evening newspaper he had been pretending to read.

"Well... just a little bit of a one." Ada went to her room, hung up her coat and hat, and then, before going back to the living room, went upstairs to make sure Mr. Meigs had got himself fresh towels—it was Wednesday, fresh-towel day. He hadn't. Then she saw that the floor of his room was littered with tiny stamp hinges.

Ada set her mouth. It had been a rotten day, working first with that doltish Mrs. Richards, who couldn't even add, and then with the stubborn manager of the civic auditorium. And then the hurried lunch, and the afternoon of phone calls, the depressing search for volunteers, and finally the long ride home on the crowded trolley. And now this—no clean towels, an untidy room, an ailing old man to look after. She had a headache, too, she discovered, but at least she'd done something to deserve hers!

She walked back downstairs and stood once more in the doorway of the living room.

"I suppose you stared yourself blind at those stamps all day," she said, "instead of taking a walk, as I told you."

"Well, I did work at them a bit," Mr. Meigs said. "I guess I got sort of...engrossed...and forgot about the walk."

"Once you start on those stamps, you forget about everything!" Ada said in annoyance. "Those stamps are killing you, that's what they're doing!"

"Oh, no...no..." Mr. Meigs protested, his head quivering negatively from side to side. He took off his glasses and rubbed his aching eyes. "No, no," he repeated.

Ada lifted her hands to her temples. "Father Meigs," she said ominously. Her mind was whirling. Clean-towel day. She thought...that stupid Mrs. Richards!...stamp hinges all over the floor...the crowded, jostling trolley...that positive idiot, Bertha Richards!

"I'm afraid you'll have to get rid of those stamps, Father Meigs," she said at last.

Mr. Meigs's mouth dropped open. He rubbed his eyes.

"I...I what?" he asked, incredulous.

"I've tried everything I know to get you outdoors," Ada said, "but you still sit in that room all day long. Your stamps are ruining your health. You'll have to get rid of them!"

"Get rid of...my stamps?" Mr. Meigs said, horrified.

The crease between Ada's eyebrows deepened. "I hate to make you do it," she said, "but if I don't, in no time at all you'll have no eyesight!"

"Why, my eyes are all right, Ada," Mr. Meigs protested. "Why...why, I've been collecting stamps all my life. It hasn't hurt my eyes."

"It's where your headaches come from, that's for certain," Ada said. She walked across the room, turned her back on Mr. Meigs, and impatiently fluffed an already perfectly fluffed pillow.

"Actually, I don't have many headaches," Mr. Meigs said.

"How about last Friday?" Ada demanded. "Don't tell me you didn't have one then."

"Just a tiny one," Mr. Meigs said. "Like this one."

"You've had others," Ada said. "Lots of them. And you'll be having more if you keep the stamps. No, they have to go. I'm sorry, but that's final."

Mr. Meigs felt very tired. "How would I pass my day, Ada," he asked quietly, "if I got rid of my stamps?"

"You can get another hobby," Ada snapped. Her own headache was throbbing viciously, right in the middle of her forehead. "Some hobby that doesn't make you use your eyes. Or your money," she added.

Mr. Meigs winced. It was true, he knew, that stamp collecting was a luxury for an elderly man who is dependent on his son and daughter-in-law for subsistence. Mr. Meigs had insisted on giving Ada half of his forty-dollar pension for room and board; the rest was quite adequate for his small expenses. About ten dollars a month went for new stamps (when he'd been younger, he'd often spent a hundred dollars for stamps, at one crack!).

"I always thought I'd leave my collection to John," Mr. Meigs said. In a way it justified the present expenditures somewhat.

"John has no time to dawdle over stamps," Ada said impatiently. "Besides, the main thing is that he expects me to look after you while he's off, and I can't do it if you're going to buck me every step of the way. I say you're killing yourself with that stamp collection, and throwing away what little money you have in the bargain. So—for your own good, mind you—out it goes! Tomorrow!"

Mr. Meigs paled at the enormity of what Ada had suggested.

He knew one thing for certain. He'd never sell the stamps. Why, it would be almost like...like selling John! John and the stamps, that was all he had.

"Dinner will be ready in fifteen minutes," Ada said. "Please be on time. I have to go out again afterward."

"Don't cook anything for me, Ada," Mr. Meigs said wearily. "I'm going to lie down. I'm not really...very hungry."

Mr. Meigs' headache was pounding ferociously by the time he reached his room. He lay down on his bed and stared up for a moment at the stains on the sagging wallboard ceiling.

Maybe Ada was just a little bit right about the stamps, he thought. Maybe he shouldn't go at them all day long. Maybe he should take a good long walk every afternoon for a while and see if it helped the headaches. But as for getting rid of the collection—well, he realized Ada had had a bad day. These committee things often made her short-tempered. But she recovered in time. Tomorrow she'd feel differently about it. She wouldn't really expect him to sell his stamps. She couldn't!

Ada wasn't home when Mr. Meigs returned from his long walk the next afternoon, and frankly, Mr. Meigs was just as glad. The walk had made him feel good, and he didn't want to chance another painful talk about the stamps—like the one at breakfast. Ada had insisted once again that he sell the stamps, and he'd come right out and defied her. He'd refused. Flatly.

It was peculiar, the feeling he had as he climbed the stairs to his room. It wasn't a premonition exactly. It was more just a thought that hadn't entered his mind before. He started to climb the stairs a little faster, and then he remembered what Dr. Fredericks had told him about taking things easy, and he slowed down again. Even so, his heart was thumping when he reached the top of the stairs and put his hand on the doorknob and turned it. He opened the door.

The six fat, red albums were gone.

Mr. Meigs sat down, breathing hard. There was no doubt about what had happened. He shut his eyes, trying to decide what to do.

He sat for nearly two hours, until half past five. Then, finally, he heard the front door slam. Slowly, he got up and descended the stairs. He found Ada standing in the front hall, examining the evening headlines.

"Ada," Mr. Meigs said calmly, evenly, "what did you do with my stamp collection?"

There was a strangely defensive tone in Ada's voice.

"I know you're not going to like this, Father Meigs," she said, "but I'm perfectly sure in my own mind that I've done the right thing for your health. I've turned your stamps over to Samuel Barnhoff, downtown, to sell."

"Ada," Mr. Meigs said through tight lips, "you have no business to do that. Those stamps belong to me."

"They were ruining your health, Father Meigs," Ada said.

Mr. Meigs exploded. "I can take care of my own health!" he roared.

"You don't seem to be able to," Ada replied curtly.

"Ada, what you've done is close to robbery!"

"Oh, fiddle!"

For a moment Mr. Meigs stared at Ada, speechless, gulping for air. Then he began to get a grip on himself.

"I'm surprised at you," he said. "You've acted most abruptly."

"I suppose you never acted abruptly?"

"Never like that."

"Oh?" Ada said. "How about last year, when suddenly you had to go fishing? Decided after lunch, and were off by two o'clock. Gone four days, too, while John and I worried ourselves sick over you. And when you finally did come back, what had you caught? Nothing but a cold!"

Mr. Meigs drew in a deep breath. He remembered. He'd taken a fishing pole along with him, all right, but he hadn't even thought about fishing. He'd spent the entire four days on a lumpy mattress in a sooty railroad hotel. It had been one of those times when suddenly, like a crashing ocean wave, the realization had broken over him that he had to get away.

"I see no connection," he said to Ada. "Whatever I've done, I've never tampered with property that wasn't mine."

"Look," Ada said, "there's no point in arguing. What's done's done. You might as well forget about it."

"I am not going to forget about it," Mr. Meigs said evenly. He started toward the telephone table at the rear of the hall. "I'm going to call Barnhoff, and I'm going to get my stamps back!"

"Oh, no you're not! I forbid you to bring those stamps back into this house!"

Mr. Meigs picked up the telephone directory and turned to the B's. From a vest pocket he produced a small magnifying glass and examined the names.

"That collection is my property," he said to the wall.

"No one ever said it wasn't," Ada said. "I'm not stealing it from you, you know. Mr. Barnhoff will send you the cheque the minute the collection is sold."

"I'm not worried about your stealing it," Mr. Meigs said coldly. "And I don't want the money. *I want the stamps!*"

Mr. Meigs waited while the number rang an even dozen times. Then he pulled his thin gold watch from his watch pocket, snapped the case open, saw that the time was a quarter till six.

For a moment he considered calling Barnhoff at his home. But then he decided that, after all, the collection was perfectly safe overnight with the broker. He could wait till morning and then—well, maybe he would go downtown and call on Barnhoff in person. It would be a lot easier to explain the situation. And anyhow, he would have to pick up the albums to bring them back. Ada would be mad as a hatter, but she'd just have to get over it.

The next morning, however, after sleeping on the matter all night, the old man got to thinking that John, after all, wasn't really a stamp fancier. In themselves, the stamps didn't mean much to him, and it might be a lot harder for John, for sentimental reasons, to dispose of the collection after Mr. Meigs passed on, than it would be for Mr. Meigs himself right now. And then there was the practical reality of the situation. He had to live with Ada from now until...well, from now on. If keeping his collection formed the basis for a feud, that would be mighty unpleasant for them all.

And besides, maybe there was something in what Ada said. Maybe he was ruining his health. Ada wasn't a bad sort—she wouldn't do this kind of thing if she didn't really, earnestly think it was for the best. Well, he'd see.

At breakfast Ada was unusually nice. She fried him two eggs, over easy, just the way he liked them, and poured him a second cup of coffee. She made no effort to hurry him and, of course, neither of them mentioned the exiled collection.

Mr. Meigs took another long walk after breakfast to try to clarify his thinking. He knew that if he was going to get his stamps back, he'd better go right away. Even now Barnhoff might be closing a deal. But on the other hand, if he actually was going to sell...

Besides, he got to thinking about the time, almost a year ago, when he and Ada had gone to a double-feature while John was in Montreal, and then—it was really a crazy thing to do—they'd gone to a midnight show right afterward. They hadn't got home till 2.30 a.m.! It had been a lot of fun, Mr. Meigs remembered. And then he remembered more soberly that there hadn't been many times like that recently. Whose fault was it, he wondered. His? Perhaps. He wasn't the perfect father-in-law, not by a long shot. Of course, it could be Ada's fault, too. Maybe it was both their faults.

Well, Mr. Meigs decided, there actually wasn't such a big hurry about making up his mind. Collections the size of his didn't sell overnight.

During the next few days Mr. Meigs did a lot of thinking, and finally, with the greatest reluctance, he made his decision. He would let Barnhoff go ahead and dispose of the collection.

It took somewhat longer to sell than Mr. Meigs had anticipated. He wondered about it from time to time, but received no word from the broker. He tried reading autobiographies and novels. Then he tried to interest himself in botany and, later, typography. And then insects. But nothing worked. He still dreamed of the stamps that had taken him on faraway journeys.

One day, when the March winds had died down, Mr. Meigs was sitting at his pine table thinking about it being the spring of his seventy-fifth year, and he decided to call on the broker. He hadn't looked at a stamp in more than two months, and he looked forward to his visit with all the hopeful anticipation a child feels for Christmas. Sam Barnhoff, whom he knew well, would probably show him some rare issues. He might even ask the broker if he could look at some pages from his own collection while he was there.

Mr. Meigs was less than two blocks from the broker's front door when a frightening thought occurred to him. It was a little the way he'd felt going upstairs the day he'd discovered his collection missing. Suppose Ada hadn't really taken his collection to Barnhoff!

He quickened his pace. The day was warm, and he was nearly out of breath by the time he entered the broker's shop. Barnhoff was standing behind the counter, a look of surprise on his face.

"Mr. Meigs!" he said. "How'd you know? I just phoned your house, but no one was home."

"Know what?" Mr. Meigs asked. His hands were shaking quite badly, and he leaned on the counter, panting.

"We just sold your collection to a big collector from Harrisville. Intact. Every blessed little stamp!"

Relief was Mr. Meigs' first sensation. At least the stamps hadn't gone astray. And then he felt a pang that the collection was now gone, eternally, beyond his reach.

"Guess how much you netted on the deal," the broker said jovially.

"Can't guess," Mr. Meigs said wearily.

The broker enunciated the sum with elaborate clarity.

"Twenty-two thousand, five hundred and forty dollars!"

"Twenty-two thousand!" Open-jawed, Mr. Meigs sat down on one of the high stools near the counter.

"You expected more?" Barnhoff asked.

"I...I..." Mr. Meigs shook his head and passed one hand across his moist forehead. "Sam, I...to tell the truth, I hadn't even thought. I mean, of course I knew they were worth something. In fact, I could tell you the catalogue value of nearly any stamp I had, but..." Mr. Meigs sighed. "When I was a young man, I used to add the values up occasionally, but...not for years, Sam, not for years."

Barnhoff nodded sympathetically. "I get it," he said.

"I guess I got so I was just collecting for the stamps themselves," Mr. Meigs said. "Not for the values, but, well, for the pleasure there was in looking at them, in filling out sets, and trying to see all the stamps I could."

"Well, you saw most of them," Barnhoff said.

Mr. Meigs's faded blue eyes looked wistfully at the neatly displayed stamps under the glass counter. "I wouldn't have guessed half that, Sam," he said.

Barnhoff smiled gently at the old man.

"I'll get your cheque ready," he said.

Before Mr. Meigs left, after an hour and a half of looking at a collection of Russian special deliveries, he asked a favor of the broker.

"Would you call Ada," he said, "my daughter-in-law, and tell her how much I got for the collection?"

"Gladly," said the broker.

"She'll be home in about three hours," Mr. Meigs said.

Ada nearly fainted with surprise when she received the broker's call. Twenty-two thousand dollars! She had a flurry of thoughts as she replaced the telephone in its cradle, some of which she was immediately ashamed of, such as the thought that the money someday, not too far off, would be inherited by herself and John. It was an unworthy thought, and she knew it. She shook her head to clear it of the vision that had flashed into her mind—the large, dignified Tudor-style house she admired so much, on the other side of town.

No, she should congratulate him. It was wonderful news for him. It might jar him out of his recent despondency and cheer him up a bit. She should go upstairs and see if he was home yet. And if he was, she should tell him how happy she was for him. And mean it.

Her feet traced the narrow trail up to the attic. She put her hand on the doorknob to the dimly lighted little room.

"Father Meigs," she called, pausing before she opened the door. "It's me, Ada." She swung the door open.

But the room was empty.

Empty save for the bare bureau and the china commode and the unpainted table and the kitchen chair. The shoes were gone, and the picture of Mr. Meigs' wife was gone, and so was the worn brown-leather toilet kit, and the military brushes with which he kept his unruly white shock under control. Everything was gone except a piece of paper on the window table.

She picked the note up with trembling hands.

"Dear Ada," it read.

"Please excuse me for rushing off without even saying good-bye. I wouldn't have, if I weren't at the age when one must hurry or else leave things undone forever." Ada sank onto the straight kitchen chair and shut her eyes. I am an awful woman, she thought. I have driven my husband's father out of my house. She looked at the note once more.

"As John can tell you," it continued, "I've always had a hankering to visit the places my stamps came from, and now at last (thanks to you, dear Ada) I'm actually going to do it!"

Thanks to you, dear Ada. Sarcasm, she wondered? But no...no, of course not, not from Father Meigs. And why, she wondered, should she now be remembering the time he'd taken her on the train to Oakville for a picnic, and to see the twenty-fourth-of-May fireworks? Why?

Her eyes stung, blurred, and for the first time (in how long?) she felt a warm tear run down her cheek.

"Until I get my passport and shots," she read presently, "my address will be Montreal—care of Postmaster, of course. Then, if I catch the right freighter, my first mail stop will be Cape Town. Think of it, Ada—Africa! I can hardly wait to get there to find presents for you and John—something that might, in some small way at least, show my deep appreciation for your many kindnesses.

"Now, you don't have to take this suggestion, Ada," the letter read, "unless you want to. But I think I'll try to put some unusual stamp issue on each letter or package I send. Could be, if you save them, they might be worth money some day! Well, God bless you both..."

Ada laid the letter down on the table and sighed. She took a handkerchief from the pocket of her skirt and blew her nose. Yes, she'd keep his letters. Of course she would. Letters, stamps, envelopes, everything. And not for their monetary value, either.

And then, suddenly, she began to laugh, not loudly, not at Father Meigs, but at herself—Ada Meigs, stamp collector!

He's Sick! He's Well! He's Sick!

The Presidential election of 1956 pitted incumbent President Dwight Eisenhower against Democratic challenger Adlai Stevenson.

In trying to unseat Eisenhower, Stevenson had a tough job. The President was popular, and the economy was robust. Eisenhower's health, however, was somewhat less robust, and the nation knew it. In September of 1955 he'd had a heart attack.

By February of 1956, however, he felt well enough to announce his candidacy for a second term. Then, in June, two months before the Republican Convention, he had an unexpected setback. He was diagnosed with ileitis, an inflammation of the small intestine. This required an operation.

The Republicans felt that only a churl would bring up Eisenhower's health as a possible impediment to his candidacy. As usual, however, churls abounded. Even though Stevenson himself was careful never to mention the topic, there was still plenty of health talk in the press and on television.

I wrote the following piece after Eisenhower had announced his candidacy, but before his intestinal problem. I liked Ike, and I certainly wished him no harm. Nevertheless, when his ileitis showed up, I had to admit—for the benefit of my article—it couldn't have come at a better time!

In August of 1956, to nobody's great surprise, the Republicans re-nominated Eisenhower. In September, my article appeared in *Atlantic Monthly*. In October, on election eve, Eisenhower's doctors gave him a clean bill of health. In November, he won in a landslide.

The most important thing about this election, however, was not Eisenhower's victory. It was the fact that Willis had sold my little essay to *Atlantic*. It not only shored up our fragile economy, but gave me confidence that the long hours I spent typing away in my dog kennel were not in vain!

September 1956, 50 cents

THE *Atlantic*

THE

CRISIS

IN TEACHING

by Oscar Handlin

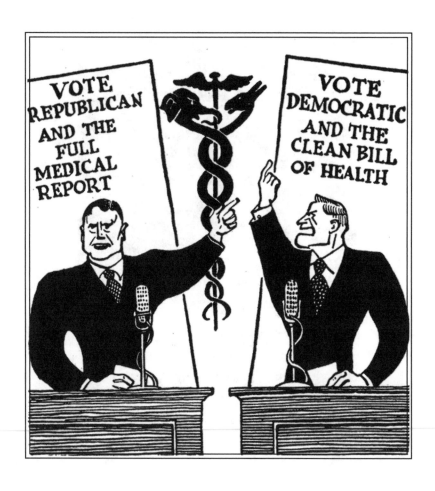

Elect the Healthiest!

Atlantic Monthly, September, 1956

In the 1968 presidential election, as a result of the three previous campaigns and their sequelae, the major parties acknowledged only one overwhelming issue: Health.

The Democrats, eager to steal a march, fired the first big gun several months before their convention. They released a survey made for them by Impartial Research, Inc., which showed that during the past eight years—four Democratic, four Republican—23.5 per cent more Republicans than Democrats died in elective office. The survey, coming on the heels of Republican ex-President Garrison's announcement of his availability, was obviously timed to catch the Grand Old Party off balance. And it did.

The following Monday, however, Garrison made the first major Republican rebuttal. In a friendly, informal television talk, he declared that not only was his own health sound, but so was the party's. He then produced an elaborate series of colored charts which purported to demolish the Democratic survey—first by demonstrating bias in the sample, and then by pointing out that the Democratic study took no account of the Accident versus Death from Natural Causes factor. More than half the Republicans dying in office, Garrison declared, were struck down not by disease but by moving vehicles—of which, he added, 61 per cent were driven by Democrats!

Bold though the speech was, two weeks later Garrison reached into the ring and withdrew his hat. At first this tended to confirm rumors that Garrison had prepared his charts with more enthusiasm than research.

The aging Alsops were not the first to point out the hollowness of this explanation. Easily a dozen Washington columnists carried the exclusive story that Garrison's recent physical had turned up a mild anemia. It then remained for the venerable Reston, in the Times, to bring to light the fact that Garrison, during the four preceding Democratic years, had suffered increasingly from nagging backache as well as from pain and distress of upset stomach.

One week later, gleeful that the popular ex-President had been forced out of the race, the Democrats convened at Chicago. There they selected Frank Dolliver Guptill to head their 1968 slate. Although Guptill, up to the time of the convention, had served only as a minor functionary, addressing envelopes, licking stamps, and the like, it was not hard, as more became known, to see why he was selected. Even the Southern Democrats, who had come to Chicago fearful that civil rights might once again split the party, found it easy to rally round a clear-eyed candidate whose blood pressure was 130 over 80, and who neither smoked nor drank.

The nonsmoking angle was getting a big play in Democratic propaganda at the time the Republican convention opened, particularly because Washington B. McDonald, the leading Republican contender since Garrison's withdrawal, had a long history of cigarette addiction, as well as a tennis elbow. Thus it was no surprise when the party solons by-passed McDonald and selected Vaughan Hardwick Timmons, Jr., as their candidate. Timmons, a vigorous stripling of thirty-eight, had never had a major illness in his life.

Timmons vs. Guptill. Guptill vs. Timmons. Even Drew Pearson would predict no more than a record vote.

Five days before the election the Democrats, who had three hundred private detectives on the job, came up with the informa-

tion that Timmons had undergone major surgery late in 1967 and
that the Republican high command had deliberately concealed
the fact.

This was the break the Republicans had been waiting for.
Jubilantly they replied that the appendectomy had not been oc-
casioned by abdominal pains or by a high white-count; on the
contrary, Timmons had voluntarily elected to have it, as a purely
prophylactic measure. Unlike Guptill, whose appendix was still
firmly (and dangerously, the Republicans hinted) attached to
his caecum, Timmons was now in a position to "better serve his
country without loss of work time due to emergency surgery."

Furthermore, said the Republicans, who had been employing
a few detectives of their own, why didn't Democratic candidate
Guptill salt his food? Was he on a low-salt diet? A *salt free* diet?
The nation deserved to know.

This was a telling blow, and Guptill took to the air waves to
answer it. Three nights before the election, in a simple, moving

speech, Guptill reviewed his medical history: Born, normal delivery. Measles at age 4, mumps at age 8, chickenpox and tonsillitis (nonrecurrent) at age 10. Minor orthodontia at age 12 to correct an overbite. Broke nose at age 14 playing touch football; set properly, septum undeviated. Green-stick fracture of the upper arm just before the eighteenth birthday, also while playing football. Inoculated at various times for smallpox, diphtheria, yellow fever, polio, hay fever. As for his abstinence from salt, it was not ominous. No one in his family—as a matter of preference and not for medical reasons—had ever used much salt.

The humble tone of Guptill's address left many a TV viewer dabbing at his eyes. The political columnists, furthermore, agreed that the Republican attack on Guptill's salt habits, far from weakening his position, had actually strengthened it.

Time was short, and the shaken Republicans grasped at straws. Chairman Alston Benedict assembled a panel of noted allergists for a half hour on TV which ended with the doctors in unanimous agreement that Guptill's hay fever shots were worthless. An ironic note is provided by the fact that, because Benedict and his confreres were so busy trying to build Guptill's two fractures into an abnormal interest in sports (portending excessive absence from the White House to participate), they entirely overlooked the fact that he had never been inoculated for tetanus.

The day before the election, Republican Timmons came down with a bad case of laryngitis and a cold. In his windup television address that night, it was obvious he was merely mouthing words that were being read by someone else.

Guptill, on the other hand, kept gaining momentum to the last. On his final 10-10:30 TV stint election eve, as a clincher, he introduced a diversified group of twelve of the nation's foremost medical specialists, and then proceeded to strip to his underwear shorts for the first complete physical in TV history.

Fourth-estate pundits who watched both broadcasts, including the rather startling barium fluoroscopy with which Guptill closed his appeal, no longer hesitated. Guptill, they predicted in stories for the morning editions, was in.

They had not reckoned with the power of television. At exactly 10:31, while Guptill was still buttoning his shirt, a cascade of glockenspiels announced the widely viewed Million Dollar Quiz. Some twelve minutes later, an untidy 65-year-old farmer from Drawstring, Arkansas, whose name was Alfred Higgins and whose category was bootlegging, came up for his $250,000 question. During the customary pre-question pleasantries, the master of ceremonies asked Higgins, facetiously, how he would stack up, were he running against Timmons and Guptill in the morrow's election.

"Well, I ain't no spring chicken," Higgins replied candidly, "and I got a leaky valve in the old pump, but I'll tell you this, young feller: If I was President, I'd sure-by-gum support all crops at 110 per cent of parity! And double that there minimum wage!"

Needless to say, Higgins, thanks to the Twenty-fifth (write-in vote) Amendment, became the nation's thirty-ninth President. He served until December 28, 1971, on which day he died of acute alcoholism, thereby leaving the 1972 election as wide open as any ever had been in the history of these United States.

After Dave Henderson's success at Smithsonian *I thought I'd try my hand at one or two of those short essays that appear on the last page of* Smithsonian, *the last page of the Sunday* New York Times Magazine, *and hardly anywhere else.*

Here's my first try. Since my agent Al Hart no longer handled anything but books, I sent it out myself. The Times *and* Smithsonian *both said no thanks. After that, I didn't know where to send it. Willis Kingsley Wing, where are you?*

A Brief History of Time

Including a breakthrough from
that li'l old watchmaker, Nike.

First, the background. The wristwatch was invented during The World War. Please don't call it The First World War. When I was a kid, it wasn't the First, it was the Only.

The wristwatch, then, was invented because, in the trenches, it was damn near impossible to fish a watch out of your heavy woolen pants, which were under your heavy woolen tunic and your heavy woolen overcoat, to see if it was time to go over the top.

Everyone clear on over the top?

The inventor of the wristwatch was probably a Brit. Basically, this Brit just took his pocket watch and stuck it on his wrist with duct tape. This made it easier to check over-the-top time than if he had to prospect for it inside his pants. Soon, however, wristwatch wearers found it was no picnic untaping the watch to take a bath or whatever, so someone cooked up a removable rig made out of leather, some holes, and a buckle. And there you have it: The Invention of the Wristwatch, a little known fact.

A Personal History of the Wristwatch. I own fifteen wrist-watches, God knows why. It simply appears that, as one journeys along through life, wristwatches accumulate.

My first wristwatch was an Elgin. It was already second-hand when my father bought it. When he gave it to me, he graduated to a second-hand Hamilton. Crack railroad engineers wore Ham-iltons, because they were noted for accuracy. The Elgin was also noted for accuracy, but was worn apparently by engineers still on the way up.

God knows where the Elgin went. My oldest extant wristwatch is a Harper, hardly a grand old name in watch biz. To compensate for any shortfall of grandeur, Harper covered its watches with positive affirmations. Mine reads: "Harper. 17 Jewels. Incabloc. Antimagnetic. Unbreakable Mainspring. All Stainless Steel. Resistant to Shock Dust and Magnetism." It hasn't run in forty years.

My next oldest watch is a Tissot. Tissot sounds classier than Harper. Not as classy perhaps as Tourneau, Girard-Peregaux, or Vacheron Constantin, but still genteel. My Tissot performed conscientiously for years. Then one day, a whimsical Fate decreed that the strap should break, the watch should fall to the asphalt of a parking lot, and I should see a Volkswagen convertible back over it. I was shattered, but not my Tissot. It still looked aristocratic when I picked it up, but its vital signs were notably absent. I kept it anyhow.

To console me, my wife gave me the watch I longed for, a Vulcain Cricket. I still wear it from time to time. Wind it up, it keeps perfect time. Set the alarm, it can wake garden gnomes.

My Bordeaux watch, also a gift, shows two goblets of wine, one red, one white. It would run if it had a new battery. So would my white Swatch and my Casio "Jogging Watch." But not my two Rolexes, the Oyster and the Cellini. Both died prematurely, possibly because I bought them from a Bangkok street vendor for $15 the pair.

We'll ignore my "Star Wars" watch, my Alarm Chronograph, and my watch with holograms on the face. But not my Timex "Stealth" watch. I bought it last year, and it's in mint condition. I still have the box and operating manual. Make an offer.

Nudging the Edge of the Wristwatch Envelope: Who would have suspected the maker of Air Jordans would be the nudger?

That's right, Nike.

My new Nike Triax is a runner's watch. I bought it, however, because I can read its GREAT BIG DIGITAL NUMBERS without my glasses. I can even read them in the middle of the night, thanks to a push-button light bright enough to help find lost objects.

But here's the *real* breakthrough. Every wristwatch designer since The Original Brit has placed his watchface at a right angle to the wrist. Check your watch, you'll see: 12 and 6 go across your arm, 9 and 3 line up with your arteries. Nike, however, has rotated the Triax watchface 20 degrees clockwise. This makes the numbers 20 degrees closer to alignment with your eyes, hence, 20 degrees easier to read. Trust me; it makes a difference. One small step for Man.

There's more, of course. Should I take leave of my senses and run a 250-lap race, my Triax will time each lap, and store the data. Later, when I'm recovering, I can play back my favorite laps. My Triax also has a stopwatch, a timer that runs backwards to zero, a counting device, and seven alarms. Why seven, I can't say. Naturally, I can't hear any of them. When they go off, however, I hear dogs barking in the next block.

All in all, it's one hell of a wristwatch. The Original Brit would be proud.

Speaker of the House

In 1957, after five wonderful years in Sonoma, we were broke. I'd written scores of short stories, some of which actually sold. It didn't cost a lot to live in Sonoma, but it cost more than I was earning.

Along with writing, I'd tried various part-time occupations to keep the wolf from the door. Our gumball-machine route *("Earn big money in your spare time!")* was the first. Our machines were scattered throughout the Sonoma and Napa Valleys, and Mary-Armour and I both worked hard at making the business succeed.

For a year and a half the route produced an indifferent stream of cash-flow. It came nowhere near the success we had so naively expected. Our greatest success was the day we sold it.

To make up for the lost revenue, small though it may have been, I tried selling correspondence courses in commercial art. Smoking was in vogue, and matchbooks were everywhere. Most matchbook covers carried advertising. One carried a picture of a face, and the seductive words:

"DRAW ME and win a free art scholarship!" Inside the matchbook was the address to which to send your drawing.

My job was to follow up on the leads these match covers generated. I found the job in the Sunday want-ads *("Earn big money in your spare time!")*. It took me to all the far reaches of the Bay Area, from Gilroy to Healdsburg and beyond.

The matchbooks led me to all kinds of neighborhoods. Thanks to my one day of training, I had a sure-fire, canned, one-size-fits-all approach.

I rang the bell. The door opened. I said:

"Hello, I'm from the *Bureau of Engraving*. Someone at this address, possibly your son, sent us a communication."

The reaction was always shocked surprise.

Bureau of Engraving? Was the kid in trouble?

I would consult my records.

"Is his name Sylvester Warble?"

Silence.

"Because if it is, he has a chance to attend a very fine professional art school. Would you like him to learn how to make really good money?"

Sylvester's mother would now be thoroughly confused.

"My company is actually called *Art Instruction, Inc.,*" I would continue. "Our parent company is called *The Bureau of Engraving*, but it has nothing to do with the U.S. Government."

This statement always brought a sigh of relief. The kid was apparently not a felon. He might, in fact—what had the man said?—he might even make some money. To a shell-shocked mother standing in an open doorway, this was a welcome thought. Preposterous perhaps, but welcome.

"Let me show you what I mean," I would say, lifting my sample book of student work and reaching tentatively for the screen door. If I was successful in worming my way into the house, I would open the book and glance around expectantly for a spot where we might look at it together.

The student sample book was fat, showy, and printed in four colors. It was very impressive. It started with the work of two graduates who were actually doing covers for *The Saturday Evening Post*. Then followed a series of glossy advertising illustrations of pretty girls, and families admiring new refrigerators. Next came samples by graduates who drew greeting cards, designed business logotypes, or did cartoons for kids' magazines. Finally, it showed the work of graduates who painted signs for a living. Some owned their own shops. Not bad, eh?

"Ma'am," I would say unctuously, "it's easy for young people with artistic talent to make a good living."

And Sylvester had talent, we knew that. Hadn't he, all on his own, drawn a very competent copy of the pretty girl on the matchbook, and sent it to us?

Sylvester didn't have to attend some expensive, faraway school, because we offered professional instruction BY MAIL. And you could pay in installments.

The trade called my canned speech my "front", and here is where it ended. I was now on my own.

I truly believed in the School. I believed it might help a kid who was headed for a stoop-labor job find a higher calling.

Much as I believed this, however, and hard as I worked, I didn't sell many courses. I could make it as far as the living room sofa, but I was not a good "closer." As a result, there was still no thumb in our leaky, financial dike.

I answered another ad and tried selling door-to-door. My new product was portable electric signs. My new market was barbershops, hardware stores, dry cleaners, or any store with a window facing the street.

The signs were attractive and simple. Essentially, they were slender, rectangular, metal cases, three to four feet long, enameled black, with fluorescent bulbs inside. Each sign came with an extensive alphabet that could be arranged along an opening on one side of the case, to make a message. The letters were colorful and transparent, mounted on opaque black backgrounds. When you turned the light on, they looked terrific.

"KID'S HAIRCUTS OUR SPECIALTY!"
"10% OFF ALL CLEANING!"
"DOUBLE GREEN STAMPS!"

In my first two weeks, walking up and down the main streets of Napa, St. Helena, and Calistoga, working full-time, I sold four signs. To survive, I needed to sell at least ten a week!

If our greatest success was the day we sold the gum route, our second greatest success was the day Simon & Schuster published my book, *The Trouble With Gumballs.* Mary-Armour and I both rejoiced at being able to hold actual copies in our hands.

There was only one problem. We'd already spent the advance. The next royalties, if any, were a year away.

In promoting the book, however, we got a nice surprise. Simon & Schuster had arranged for me to appear on *"Cavalcade of Books,"* a TV show filmed live in Los Angeles. Appearing on local television was nice, but Mary-Armour and I both felt the book needed national exposure. So, while in L.A., we dropped by the offices of John Guedel Productions. Guedel produced the highly popular comedy-quiz show, *You Bet Your Life,* starring Groucho Marx.

I met one of the show's producers, gave him a copy of the book, and we drove back to Sonoma. Two weeks later we got a call. Groucho wanted us both on the show.

We had a great time at the filming. Groucho was extremely nice to us, and we felt the national exposure would undoubtedly help book sales.

The most important result, however, was that we won $2,100. That's right, $2,100! In 1956 terms, that was a small fortune.

Our prize consisted of $2,000 for answering Groucho's question, "Who was the Supreme Allied Commander in World War One?", plus fifty bucks apiece for saying the Magic Word. The Magic Word was "clock." As four cameras ground away and the audience cheered, Groucho's duck came down from the ceiling with the money clenched in his bill.

The Supreme Allied Commander in WWI? Why, Marshall Foch, of course. But you knew that already.

Groucho's fiscal transfusion was a great boost. What was

more, we got a letter from Willis Wing saying I'd sold two more stories. Were we going to make it after all?

The answer was no. Judgment day came. In the early summer of 1957, Mary-Armour and I faced the hard truth. Our bank account was running on fumes.

"I'll get a job," I said.

Selling art courses, of course, had been a job. Selling electric signs had been a job, too.

"A *real* job," I said.

The only real jobs appeared to be in San Francisco. I had no doubt I could get one. The only question seemed to be: What did I want to be when I grew up?

I decided I would become an advertising copywriter. I was a writer of sorts already. What more did you need? Besides, according to books and movies, advertising was glamorous, highly-paid, and lots of fun.

After 29 fruitless interviews, I hit pay dirt on the 30th. Further, I was to not going to be "just a copywriter." I was to be a copy chief! What a title! The agency, consisting of a dozen people, was called Hoefer, Dieterich & Brown.

It didn't matter that I was a chief with no Indians. I didn't care. I had a job. I was the agency's first full-time copywriter. I would write copy for four account executives who had previously written their own copy. Best of all, I was going to be paid—regularly—in actual U.S. dollars!

I liked the job. I liked the people. I had no idea what the agency's production department did, nor its media department, but that was okay. I could learn as I earned.

Time passed, the agency grew. The chief got his first Indian. The agency grew some more. He got his second.

As I began to understand more about the business of advertising, I discovered I had lots of opinions. I had opinions about what made good ads and bad ads. I had opinions about advertising research. I had opinions about—you may think it's an oxymoron—advertising ethics. I was, in fact, so full of opinions about my new occupation I wanted to tell the world.

I wrote a speech. I called it, *"Does God Approve of Advertising?"*

Under that umbrella I ranged far and wide. I quoted Oscar Wilde: *"An idea that is not dangerous is not worthy of being called an idea at all."* I quoted George Bernard Shaw: *"The reasonable man adapts himself to the world. The unreasonable man persists in trying to adapt the world to himself. Therefore, all progress depends on the unreasonable man."* Heady stuff indeed.

I showed my speech to my boss, John Hoefer. He liked it. He said I should deliver it to the San Francisco Advertising Club. He made some calls, pulled a few strings, and on March 25th, 1959, I became a Luncheon Speaker.

Ad Club luncheon speakers sit at a raised head table in a banquet room at the Sheraton-Palace Hotel. If they look up, they see 150 Ad Club members munching hungrily in a sea of white tablecloths. If they look down they see creamed chicken and peas.

The club president made announcements and introduced the head table luminaries. Finally, he introduced the program chairman, and the program chairman introduced me.

I moved to the podium. Half the members were now puffing on cigarettes—it was still okay then. Nervously, I faked a smile.

I thanked the program chairman for his kind introduction, and started my speech. I surveyed my audience. Nobody looked openly hostile.

I finished my first paragraph, which ended with a tiny joke. The audience laughed. It was a miracle! The audience was supposed to laugh, and they actually did!

I began to relax. I was amazed to find it was not so hard after all. I liked the speech I'd written, and it was fun to deliver it to an audience that laughed in the right places.

And so I found a new career. Not instead of advertising, but in addition to advertising. I was a public speaker.

With that speech I found out something else. If you give a speech and not too many people fall asleep, you will be asked to give the same speech again. In some cases, again and again and again.

The world is full of frantic program chairmen, desperately trying to fill their schedules for June, October, or February next year. When invited, all you have to do is dust off your most recent talk, and write a new intro that gives the impression you wrote your speech specifically for delivery to the California Elementary Schools Administrators Association. I did that, and found myself on a podium in Sacramento, and—totally unexpected—getting an honorarium!

Not long after my Ad Club speech I got a letter from the 4A's—the American Association of Advertising Agencies. The 4A's represented advertising's "big time." Every major advertising agency in the U.S.—and many of the serious minors, including ours—was a member. They invited me to speak at their three-day regional meeting in Santa Barbara.

Obviously, for this event I couldn't just recycle *"Does God Approve of Advertising?"* Four creative directors from Eastern agencies would be speaking the same morning I spoke, and I didn't want to look like a bumpkin. It was obvious I needed something new.

That is the origin of the speech in the next chapter. I worked hard writing it. I dug up a lot of print ads, I shot a lot of slides. I wrote. I rewrote. I rehearsed in front of Mary-Armour, and incorporated her good suggestions.

The day before the conference Mary-Armour and I drove to Santa Barbara with John and Kay Hoefer, and checked into The Biltmore. The first day of the conference we had a jolly time eating, drinking, playing tennis together, and listening to other speakers. The second day was quite different. It was my turn to stand and deliver.

Quaking just a bit, I did stand, and I did deliver my premiere rendition of *"1992."*

I won't be modest. *"1992"* got a standing ovation. I was enormously relieved. I also found I had many new friends. Before the speech, a big-time media rep whom Mary-Armour had known as a child in Rye was friendly, but too busy to get together with us for a drink. After the speech, he invited us to dinner—"tonight, tomorrow night, what's good for you?"

But enough about you. Let's move on to the next chapter, and talk about me for a change.

1992

1992

*A speech presented to the
American Association of Advertising Agencies
Santa Barbara Biltmore, October 19, 1959*

On the 21st of October, 1992, after the radiation had cooled off on the planet Earth, a spacecraft from the planet Venus, powered by a mixture of Boron, Petrox, and Geritol Junior, landed at the site of what had once been New York City.

The first men out of the airlock were a pair of Venusian anthropologists, one named Gamma-25, the other named Rock Hudson-77.

The two anthropologists had made the trip, over a long weekend, in the hope of substantiating their pet theory. It was their belief, that since the Earth and Venus were both fragments from the same interstellar explosion—and had, therefore, started off with the same mineral elements, the same atmosphere, and the same amoebas—it was quite possible that the two planets had developed along similar lines.

Unfortunately, the two scientists found nothing. No bones, no buildings, no artifacts. Of the great cities that to Venusian telescopes had appeared as bright spots on the face of the planet—New York, Chicago, Santa Barbara—there was now only sand, water, and fused metals. Of the great highway system that Venusian astronomers had observed on clear nights, stretching across the great North American continent, there remained nothing, not even a beer can or a Kleenex.

Gamma and Hudson were, of course, greatly disappointed. In fact, in no time at all they reached the point where they began telling one another it really didn't matter—what the heck, they'd had the trip, hadn't they? And wasn't it a relief to get away from the wife and kids? And then they found it.

"It" was a manila envelope, lying between two thick sheets of lead.

Gamma and Hudson, of course, had no way of knowing that it had been left, quite accidentally, in a radiologist's office just before the blast, by an account executive who was having pictures taken of his stomach. In it—the envelope, that is, not the stomach—were a number of tearsheets of magazine advertisements.

The two anthropologists, jubilant over this sudden reversal of their fortunes, felt a new surge of confidence. After all, these two gentlemen were the same pair who had painstakingly reconstructed the entire skeleton of an early Martian, through having found one bone of the big toe. Thus, with their new find, they knew they would have no trouble reconstructing an accurate picture of the Earth people, their habits, their customs, their culture.

After a year of study, the two scientists made a preliminary report of their findings, before the annual meeting of the Academy of Associated Amateur Anthropologists—known on Venus as the 4A's.

"It's a shame," Gamma reported in his portion of the program, and I quote, "It's a shame we've never been able to crack the language. We thought we were on the right track for a while until we came up with a translation that read, 'low in tar, with more taste to it.' As this obviously made no sense, we threw out all our work up to that point, and made a fresh start."

It was anthropologist Hudson's job to comment on the visual portion of the findings. "Earth people," he reported, and again I quote, "Earth people were, in many ways, exactly like us Venusians. They looked like us; they lived in the same kinds of houses; even the tailfins of their automobiles bore a striking resemblance to our own.

"The similarity ends there, however. It is strictly physical. Because, from a mental and emotional point of view, Earthlings and Venusians are planets apart.

"Take, for example," he said, flipping on his slide machine, "this picture of home life among the Earth people."

"As you view it, consider, if you will, what would happen if this situation occurred in your family here on Venus.

"It's Saturday, and you've put on a nice, clean pair of khaki trousers. You've spent the morning applying a careful coat of paint to your living room wall. You've nearly finished the job. And then your small daughter comes in, leans one smudgy hand against the wall you've slaved over, grabs a paintbrush in the other, and begins to paint your knee.

"DUTCH BOY" INSTANT

Needs no smoothing out...
no extra cover-up work...
starts drying instantly!

"Well, you know how you'd feel! And you know what you'd say, too! But on Earth, a happening of this kind merely amuses the father and makes him smile fondly...

"or...

"...take the other half of this ad. A small boy is pointing out the fact that the family dog is about to scamper through the tray that holds the paint for Mom's roller. Following this action, the dog will undoubtedly make a circuit of the living room rug, leaving little turquoise footprints.

"Does this faze Mom? Not in the least. She smiles and goes on painting.

"Truly, these Earthlings were an heroic race!

NALPLEX

"They were a race, too, with a tremendous capacity for extracting pleasure from little daily acts which we here on Venus might consider routine, or boring, or both.

"Take, for example, the act of washing...

"Here is an Earth-woman washing her hair. Is she bending over and squinting to keep the soap out of her eyes? No, she is not. She is, in fact, having a ball. She is experiencing Deep-Down Satisfaction."

"So is this Earth-child."

106

"And so is this Earth-Dad, whom we see here, grinning happily at his reflection in the mirror."

"Here is the same Earth-Dad getting Deep-Down Satisfaction from shaving. Note that he makes no funny faces to stretch his skin taut, nor does he inflate his cheek. The really unusual thing about this photograph, however is the fact he is as calm as he is. For, you will note he is in a shower, and for most people, the shower...

"...or any kind of splashing water...induced a kind of pleasure that went well beyond the level of Deep-Down Satisfaction, and often verged on...

"...inebriation...

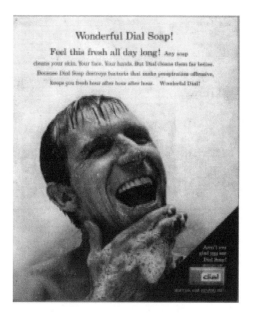

"...animal frenzy...

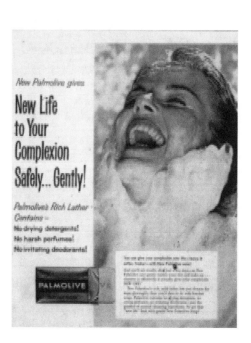

"...or even an ecstasy almost too private to photograph."

Why you need a kitchen extension phone

BELL TELEPHONE SYSTEM

"A more sedate Earth-pleasure, a sort of emotional pick-me-up enjoyed primarily by the women, was achieved through the use of an instrument that would correspond roughly, I'd say, to our Venusian telephone.

"If, for example, the kids started to mess things up in the kitchen, the harried housewife had merely to pick up the telephone and start listening. Within seconds, she would start to smile.

"This remedy was equally effective for other minor irritations, as for example, when things started to fall out of the hall closet..."

"I just had to call you first thing to tell you how much fun we had!"

REACH FOR THE TELEPHONE
and share the news

BELL TELEPHONE SYSTEM

"We have, of course, no way of knowing what soothing message was broadcast by the Earth-telephone.

"We do know this, however, that while the Earth-phone seems to have been equipped with a mouthpiece, no one has ever been observed speaking into it...

"They all just listen...

"...and smile...

"...and smile...

"...and smile."

"I have spoken earlier of how certain routine actions—washing, for example—could change an Earthling's whole outlook on life. Similarly, there were certain common objects that triggered emotional responses that we on Venus could duplicate only through the use of tranquilizing pills.

Sta-Puf restores softness, fluffiness to all your loveliest washables

M-m-m, that special Cannon feel
—such luxurious towels, such marvelous buys at *1.00
The soft beauty is woven in to last for years

"Take towels, for example...

"Five minutes ago, this Earth-woman and her daughter were arguing heatedly over whether it was, or was not, time for the girl to practice her piano lesson.

"On Venus, this situation could have ended only in sharp words and tears. On Earth, however, the wise mother merely got out a stack of bath-towels, pressed one to her cheek, and gave the rest to her daughter...

"As you can see from their state of dreamy complacency, the treatment was 100% effective."

"Unfortunately, we don't know what has driven these three women to take to their towels. It has been suggested by my colleague, Dr. Gamma, that they are actually the same woman, and that she is checking the T.Q., or Tranquility Quotient, of three separate towels.

"Obviously, they all score pretty high."

"Not so high, perhaps, as this lady's towel, which has induced a state of near-coma."

"The Earth-practice of feeling towels may, of course, have been tied up with the Earth-woman's need to feel secure. Speaking of which...

"...here's a woman feeling an honest-to-goodness security blanket. She's obviously very calm and happy and well-adjusted."

"And here's a woman getting quite a nice, high sensation from pressing a double handful of cotton cosmetic balls against her throat and chin."

"Feeling blankets and cotton cosmetic balls, however, never achieved the popularity of towel feeling, and many women amassed quite large towel collections."

"There, were other fine Earth-hobbies, too, however."

"Here, for example, is a man photographed with his collection of whiskey bottles...

"...and here is a woman whose hobby is saving vacuum cleaners. Notice how she has worked out a very artistic arrangement of them in her living room."

"Living rooms on Earth, incidentally, seldom contained much furniture, as the Earth-people seemed to derive more pleasure from sitting, and in some cases, lying, on the floor."

"Here, for example, is a typical Earth-family getting its kicks simply from lying on the rug and looking at it..."

"Here is another example, a young lady lying on her rug, enjoying it to the fullest. Actually, she is getting twice the normal pleasure, as she is simultaneously talking on the telephone. To go even further, we might assume, from her careless and somewhat suggestive pose, that she has recently been feeling her towel. But on the other hand, as my colleague Dr. Gamma has pointed out, this picture ...

"...and this one...may simply be indications of a rather primitive form of rug worship."

"If this is so, however, we will have to assume that other floor coverings were worshipped, too, inasmuch as...

...we have here a young lady who is getting much the same reaction as the rug sitters, even though she is sitting on a piece of cold, hard linoleum..."

"Eating on the floor was very popular on Earth, not only among the younger set...

"...but among their elders."

"Much as Earth-couples enjoyed eating on the floor, however, they derived even more enjoyment...as why shouldn't they...

118

"...from just *lying* on the floor with their heads together.

"This held true, and the lovers were equally comfortable, whether they were lying on a rug, or...

"...simply lying on a thin layer of vinyl tile...

"...laid over a concrete slab."

"Earth-children were as carefree and as easily amused as their elders. All you had to do to keep them happy was to...

"...open the refrigerator and let them take a look at the vegetables...

"...or..."

"...you could open the dishwasher and show them a nice, big, clean plate.

...Or, if you wanted to keep the whole gang spellbound for hours...

"...you could pour something from a paper bag."

"One last note on Earth-women: There is reason to believe that there flourished on Earth a tribe of exceedingly athletic women, women who were ten to twenty times more active than the average. At least that's the conclusion we draw from seeing this same group of them constantly...

"...at the stable...

"...doing ballet numbers...

New Kotex napkins with the Kimlon center
protect better, protect longer.

"...sailing...

"...surfing...

"...skin-diving, and so on.

SPLASH
RIGHT IN!

Don't miss a single day of fun!
Do what you want—even swim—wearing Tampax!
Millions use it. Worn internally, it's the modern way!

TAMPAX

SO MUCH A PART OF YOUR ACTIVE LIFE

"Until we crack the language, however, I'm afraid the riddle of their great activity will have to remain unsolved."

NOTHING IS BEYOND YOU

Not even swimming
...on any sunlit day you care to dare the deep!
Like millions, you use Tampax! Worn internally, it's the modern way!

TAMPAX

SO MUCH A PART OF YOUR ACTIVE LIFE

"This bring us, rather logically, I believe, to the question of why these Earth-people, who resemble us Venusians so much in appearance and achievements, are so completely different in custom and temperament. As is frequently the case, medicine supplies the answer. These people needed the psychic comforts we've discussed, because they were peculiarly susceptible to many frightening diseases.

"Imagine, for example, the suffering endured by this poor chap. Forget for a moment his pain, evident in panel number three. Forget his worry. Forget the drain on his financial resources, and think about this one aspect of his suffering, visible in panel number four...

"...namely, the embarrassment of having a disease in which the nasal passages, and heaven knows what other internal organs, light up from within, and are visible to bystanders!

"It was natural though, that disease should have struck Earth-people so hard. The reasons become clear when you realize how they were constructed internally.

"At the bottom of this advertisement for example, is a side view of an Earth-man's digestive apparatus...

"In the picture below, we see a front view."

"It takes a lot of rugs...it takes a lot of telephones...it takes a lot of bath towels to make up for having insides like that! Gentlemen of the Venusian Academy, be doggone glad you're Venusians!"

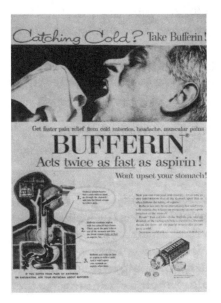

There is, unfortunately, no record of whether Gamma and Hudson were knighted, or thrown out of the Academy. And before you do either to me, let's see if there's a reasonable answer to a question that may be lurking in some of your minds, namely, "Why is this guy making so much fun of these ads, which represent a lot of time and money and blood and sweat and tears, and a lot of other things besides?"

Well, the answer is this: That while one or two of these ads may deserve better treatment than I've given them, the rest of them just aren't talking to people. They're certainly not talking to me, and I have an idea they're not talking to you, either.

To whom are they talking, then? Themselves.

Of course, there's nothing wrong with talking to oneself. I'm told it means you have money in the bank. This is certainly true for the advertisers whose ads I've just shown you. Look back over the list, and you'll find it contains some of the biggest advertisers in the country.

What else is wrong with these ads? Partly, they suffer from being imitative. Partly, from addressing themselves not to flesh and blood, but to a set of statistics. Partly, from being a marriage of the insignificant with the unbelievable.

In short, they're dull. And dullness, as any novelist, playwright, or editor will tell you, is the kiss of death. Dullness is what makes The Prospect, seated in his comfortable living room, turn the little knob, or the big, expensive color page, or the cold, cold shoulder.

Besides, unlike the jolly, enthusiastic Earth-people in the ads, most of us bore rather easily. We get tired of the thousands of visual cliches thrown at us daily. So tired, in fact, the only reaction these images inspire is a glazed eye and a yawn.

Speaking as a committee of one, I get tired, for example, of beer ads in which an unseen hand has just finished pouring a glass perfectly full of amber liquid.

I get tired of otherwise realistic ads in which the models hold cans or bottles by the itty-bitty tips of their fingers, so they won't cover any part of the sacred label.

And speaking of realism, you have no idea how cranky I get when I'm asked to believe that the studio-photographed model is really where the faked-in background implies she is.

I get tired, too, of seeing people in ads get such a big charge out of activities I know are a bore to most people, such as ironing, opening and closing oven doors, polishing cars, loading dishwashers, pointing at soaps, or taking The Product off the super-market shelf.

I get tired of those men in white coats with pencils and clip-boards. You know the ones I mean—they're always putting the advertiser's product through some grueling test, which it invari-ably passes well ahead of all competition.

And I get tired of models. I get awfully tired of that girl with the little mole right here—you know the one. And the male mod-els—there was one I counted in five different ads in the same issue of the New Yorker. But mostly I get tired of those perfectly perfect models, the kind that never perspire or spit or go to the bathroom, and who don't go to bed at night, they just go back into their case.

In other words, I get tired of seeing people in ads who live a life that seems to bear absolutely no relationship to my life, or to the life of anyone I know. I see ads like that and all I can do is shake my head and figure: I must be missing something.

I know this: The advertiser is missing something. Me. Me, multiplied by countless indifferent millions.

I realize it's always easier to tear things down than to build them up. And I realize it's probably incumbent on me to offer some constructive message to the people who produce the kind of unreal, unbelievable ads I've been griping about.

My message is simply this: Quit smoking that stuff. Get back in touch with reality. Go outdoors and talk to some real people. Find out what kind of thing really makes their eyes light up, and makes them say, "Gee whiz! Look at that!"

I'll tell you this: It's not a new gadget for cleaning a john.

I am well aware, of course, that there are, on the other hand, agencies and advertisers who do maintain contact with reality, who do take the trouble to try to communicate with me in their ads, who do recognize that I'm an individual and not a Mass Market, and who try to talk to me with sense, with humor, with dignity, with sincerity. To those agencies and advertisers, I, as a consumer of advertising, am truly grateful.

It's 4:80—How About Lunch?

Time is wonderful. It's free, and it runs on endlessly with no subsidies or special-interest legislation. So why do we have such an archaic system for describing it?

Our system starts out okay. The basic unit is one day—midnight to midnight. That's clean and sensible. But then we break it into 24 smaller units, hours. Why 24? Where'd that come from? Then we divide each hour by 60, a number that comes from the same grab-bag as 24. Each day becomes 1,440 minutes long, not a very tidy number.

Next, we divide each minute by 60. What is it with 60 anyhow?

Days, hours, minutes, seconds. It's like telling time in gallons, quarts, pints, and ounces. Or bushels and pecks, or furlongs. All these systems need an overhaul. Since we can't fix them all at once, I propose we start with time.

To have a clean, sensible time system, we've got to go metric. Except for time, most of the world is already metric. We're the big holdout. We have metric currency and metric liquor bottles, which is a blessing, but that's about it.

Making time metric will encourage our acceptance of the other stuff—the meters, the kilometers, the whole kit. Here's another advantage: Since nobody uses metric time—yet—we'll get credit for leading the way. Europe, China, the rest of the world will all be grateful. They're mired in the 24-60 swamp, too.

In going metric we have two choices. One is the single 10-hour day, stretching from midnight to midnight. Or, stretching from noon to noon, because when midnight happens depends on when noon happens, not the other way around. But we can take our pick. When you're starting fresh, you can go any way you want.

Our second option is to have two 10-hour half-days, just as we now have two 12's. One runs from midnight to noon, the other noon to midnight.

This option might make the plan easier to sell at home and abroad. It's not as elegant as the single 10-hour day, but we can't ignore marketability.

Here's how it would work.

Let's say Donald Trump, to pick a name at random, currently gets up at 7:30 a.m. Under the new system he would get up at 6:25. The sun would be in the same place in the sky, and he would have slept just as long, but he would *feel* he'd gained an extra hour and five minutes. Multiply that by 365, and he'll build three extra Trump Something-or-Others every year.

As usual, Don would be ready for lunch at high noon. High noon would occur, as always, when the sun crossed directly overhead somewhere in Donny's time zone. God knows where that place is, but that's another story.

High noon, of course, would be called 10:00 o'clock. The minute before high noon would be 9:99. I'm sure you figured out long before now, the metric hour has 100 minutes.

If, under the old system, Donny hung around the office till 5:00 p.m., he could now leave at 4:17. That's got to feel good. If he watches TV till bedtime—11 p.m., old style—he would now be tucking in at 9:16. It wouldn't actually *be* earlier, but it would *seem* earlier. How's that for a system!

The answer is: Very, very good.

Superior as this system is, though, we still have to ask: Why two 10-hour half-days? Isn't two binary? Doesn't giving prominence to the number two contaminate a system based on 10? I propose, therefore, a pure metric system. A pure metric system will make 10 beautifully simple hours do all the work currently handled by 24 messy ones.

The system may take some getting used to. For example, if you now get up at 7:30 a.m., under the new system you'll rise at 3:12. Not 3:12 a.m., not 3:12 p.m., just 3:12. That could be off-putting. But not for long.

You'll still have lunch at high noon. That will be reassuring. Only now we'll call it 5 o'clock.

We'll grow used to hearing people say, "Hey, it's 4:80—how about lunch?"

Here's further reassurance. Let's say you now eat dinner at 6:00. With the new system, you'll eat at 7:50. Upsetting? Certainly not. And if you like the sophisticated sound of "Dinner at Eight", just delay your dinner 14 old-style minutes. *Voila*!

Metric midnight? Ten o'clock, of course.

Before long, you'll *like* the sound of the new time.

"It's ten o'clock...the witching hour!"

"I'm so sleepy. I was up till 9:85 last night!"

"I'll be home by half past ten, Daddy..."

"10:50? No way, young lady! I want you home by midnight!"

Well, that's my proposal. The 10-hour, 1,000-minute day. Neat, trim, and metric.

Scoffers may say it's too radical. I beg to differ. As a nation, we're nothing if not flexible. We'll be loving the new system before we know it!

Incidentally, there's no need to thank me for inventing it. I like to think of it as giving something back.

Three days after 9.11 I went into our garage looking for a screwdriver. As I turned to go back into the house, I saw something on the floor. It was the 15-cent stamp above.

How this ancient stamp chose that time to make its appearance I'm not sure. It took my breath away. The cancellation unmistakably represented the Twin Towers falling, while the Statue of Liberty stood between them, her torch steady.

9.11.01

Like everyone else, Mary-Armour and I were shocked and surprised by the tragedy of September 11, 2001. We were saddened anyone could be so angry with us they could even think about doing such a deed.

At the time, we were holding tickets to fly to New York on September 13th. On arrival, we were to be driven to a remote hostelry called Lake Mohonk Mountain House, in New Paltz, New York. For nearly a year we had been planning a gathering with the nine other surviving members of a Yale group that had originally numbered 15, and our wives.

When the September 11th tragedy occurred, we pondered what to do. With a bravado we weren't sure we really felt, we decided we wouldn't let terrorists keep us from attending.

United Airlines, however, had other plans for us. They cancelled our flight. We rebooked for the following day. They cancelled again. By the time they were ready to take us, the New Paltz gathering was over. Seven couples had been able to get there by car. Three, including us, had not.

Earlier, our leader Jim Howard had suggested we each present some sort of memoir at the gathering. I had packed pens and pads so I could write mine on the plane to New York.

When there was no plane, I felt I needed no memoir. However, as copies of memoirs by those who had attended the gathering started to arrive in the mail, my guilt kicked in. I decided I'd better write one, too, about *something*, and send it to the other members.

So I did, as you will see by turning the page.

This is an ash pit, a relic from the days when every house in Denver had one. This one has some fancy concrete blocks on top, probably an effort to shield the backyard from the alley. Denver outlawed ash pits many years ago to deal with a serious smog problem. Few remain. This one should be given Historic Landmark status.

The Ash Pits of Denver

Everyone was writing a memoir. I had to write one, too. It was the middle of the night, and I wanted to sleep, but my mind wouldn't let me.

"What will you write about?" it asked. "Your spiritual journey? Your great deeds of public service? That won't take long."

That's when I found myself thinking about the ash pits of Denver. I had been thinking earlier about the Jehovah's Witnesses. Before that, Buddhism. Could it be I'd had a spiritual journey after all?

I was born in the front bedroom of 457 High Street in Denver. Williams Street was parallel to High, on the other side of the block. Between the two streets was a narrow alley with garages and fences. And ash pits.

Ours was typical. Brick, five feet high, five wide, five deep. Cement top, circular hole in the center.

One of my boyhood jobs was to empty wastebaskets into the ash pit. When my father ignited it, the pit smoldered for days.

Summer or winter, the ash pit never lost its special smell of burnt rubbish. It was mostly paper, with overtones of half-burnt wood, scorched paint, and the acrid odor that comes from the incomplete combustion of slick magazines.

Sometimes, in dumping wastebaskets, I accidentally threw away a treasure. A toy, a Big-Little Book, a priceless copy of

Aero Digest. My older brother and I built model aircraft. He subscribed to *Aero Digest* to keep us current on the designs of Schneider Cup racers.

This kind of tragedy was seldom terminal. On the alley side of the ash pit there was a small opening at ground level. Through this hole, once or twice a year, the ash man emptied the ash pit. If you cared enough about your lost object, you could lie on the extremely grubby ground outside the hole and fish around inside with the garden hoe. With luck, you might reclaim your treasure.

Forever after, of course, your toy, your Big-Little Book, your Aero Digest smelled of ash pit. It was a small price to pay, however, for retrieving the plans—front view, side view, top view—of some important airplane.

During the Depression the ash pit served other functions. It was the place where hungry men chalked signs to warn of a vicious dog, or to mark a likely place to get a handout. The back door of 457 High was a likely place.

Which brings us closer to Jehovah's Witnesses. But not much.

From early childhood I attended Church of the Ascension, three blocks from home. I didn't know it, but I was a high-church Episcopalian. I was an ideal member. I attended Sunday School, and when I was older I served at Communion. I lit the altar candles with a taper on a long pole, I brought wine and water on command, and I doused the candles when we were through.

I had an occasional tendency to faint during the service, or sometimes get a nosebleed. The fainting presumably came from hunger, it being a no-no to eat breakfast before Communion. It was an inconvenience of sorts for the priest, who had to pour holy water on my forehead to revive me. Still, volunteers being in short supply, when Father Wolcott could find no other possible acolyte, I got the call.

I liked young Father Wolcott. And I liked venerable, asthmatic, old Father Foster. I'm not sure which one of them it was who told me, in answer to my question, that no, my dog Spot who had just died would not go to heaven.

It seems such a small thing. Why do I still remember it after all these years? It was a speed bump. In fact, it was more than a speed bump, it was like hitting an iceberg. My Episcopalian ship didn't sink but I started the pumps.

When I turned 13, nevertheless, there was a shortage of church volunteers, so I became a Sunday School teacher. My students were boys three years younger than I, spirited and rambunctious. I am happy to say I received numerous compliments for my extraordinary ability to keep them quiet. You could see us through the glass doors that opened off the main parish hall, and it was clear I had their attention.

I never revealed that I read to them—as the only possible means of keeping them in their chairs—not from the Lesson, but from my brother's copy of *Tales of the Supernatural*.

A spiritual change overtook me when I entered High School. I found I was going to more dances, movies, amusement parks, and beefsteak fries (welcome to Colorado!) than church services. Saturday night eclipsed Sunday morning.

At Yale, as far as I can remember, I attended church once. I went alone to one of the churches on the Green. I listened to the music, the prayers, the sermon, the supplications, the voice tones, the organ tones, and I felt vaguely distressed. Something was wrong. I had become a spectator.

Life speeded up. Suddenly I was out of college, into the Navy, out of the Navy, finding a job, living in Manhattan. Churches were just buildings I passed on my way to work.

I fell in love. Mary-Armour agreed to marry me. What joy! Her father was an Episcopalian, her mother a Presbyterian. Not my problem. Either way, we were headed for a church. It turned out to be Christ Presbyterian in Rye, New York. Some of you will remember it.

We lived on East 53rd Street. I can't remember going to church, except on visits to Rye, until Jamie came along. Then, a baptism happened. It was a very nice event. Jamie wore an ancestral baptismal dress, and there was a very nice luncheon afterwards.

When Jamie was six months old, Mary-Armour and I bought a White cab-over-engine truck. We loaded Jamie and our furniture into it, and moved to Sonoma, California. It took years before we realized what a cruel blow we had struck his maternal grandparents by absconding with their only grandchild. All we could think of was our grand adventure.

In Sonoma, new friends introduced us to the Episcopal Church. We liked the church. We liked the pastor, an ancient Briton who reminded me of Father Foster. We attended, and I began to feel Episcopalian again.

The church had a very active group of young adults. My strongest memories of this Church are not of Sundays, but of Saturday nights.

I'll agree this sounds pretty shallow. Nevertheless, on those Saturday nights we made some friendships that became important parts of our lives for years to follow.

We lived in Sonoma five years. I wrote fiction and did odd jobs. My agent in New York sold my book and a fair number of my stories, but, in 1957, we ran out of money.

I needed a job. The good jobs were in San Francisco. We moved to San Rafael in Marin County, a good place from which a fledgling copywriter could commute.

Mary-Armour had always felt our children—three of them now—should have a grounding in the Christian faith. I agreed. We began to attend Christ Presbyterian Church in Terra Linda, and the children went to Sunday School. The Saturday night party structure of the Sonoma Episcopalians was notably absent, but the people were likable and friendly. We were glad to be among them. We were church people again.

The deal-breaker came when it was time to baptize our fourth child, Rebecca.

We both loved Jim Upshaw, the affable young pastor of Christ Presbyterian. We went to him happily to arrange the day when he, in front of the entire congregation, would make Rebecca one of the flock. Jim wanted to run through the baptism ceremony a few days beforehand, so we would know what to do and say. Thus we arrived at that part of the ceremony in which we, as Rebecca's parents, would acknowledge her sins. These would then be washed away by the baptism.

I said, "Jim, is that an absolutely necessary part of the ceremony? Rebecca's a little baby, just brought into the world. She hasn't had time to work up any sins. I don't want to say it."

"Well, Jim," he said patiently, and off we went. He explained original sin, and we debated this proposition: Resolved, that Rebecca has sins that need to be washed away. He took the Affirmative, I took the Negative. Neither of us would let go.

On baptism Sunday, therefore, Mary-Armour stood alone before the congregation, holding Rebecca. The ceremony proceeded, and I watched, keeping their seats warm till it was over.

I admired Mary-Armour for her stand. She was a pragmatist. She said, "I don't care what I have to say. I just want to get this baby baptized." And she did!

Somehow, the incident was a catalyst to my thinking. I didn't care how many priests, bishops, councils, and synods had legislated the subject during the past 2,000 years. I knew all of them were wrong. And I knew they were wrong when they said people in India and China and Africa weren't "going to heaven" because, sadly, they had never had the opportunity to become followers of Jesus. I felt sure that wasn't Jesus's point of view!

It's strange how your feelings about God can develop at a subconscious level, without your being aware. This brings us back to the Jehovah's Witnesses, and to the Saturday afternoon when, as they had done many times before, two attractive, young Witnesses knocked at our door.

"Good afternoon," one of them said. He had his copy of *The-*

Watchtower at the ready. "We're calling in your neighborhood to help people get ready for when Jesus comes back. We'd like to give you our magazine to help you prepare for our Lord God's return to earth."

"God's return?" I said.

"Yes," he said, "we're not sure when, but we feel it will be soon. Do you feel you're prepared ?"

I thought my religious feelings had been dormant, but I discovered my approach to God had undergone a great sea-change.

"I've got news for you," I said, "You don't have to wait."

"Beg pardon?" said the Witness.

"He's here now," I said. "He was never away. He's been here all the time."

The lead Witness opened his mouth, but I kept going.

"He's not just *with* us," I said, "he's *in* us. He's in me, he's in you, he's in all of us. He's in that cat over there—see him there, he's sleeping under the juniper. And he's in the juniper itself. And he's in the dirt and the rocks and the air, he's everywhere!"

"But..." said the Witness.

"He's always been here," I said. " He's everywhere at once. All over the world. We all live in a place called 'God.'"

I went on. "Maybe he's a she," I said. "I don't know. Anyhow, you just have to try to understand his or her ways, and be grateful."

The Witness didn't say anything for a few moments. He looked at his pretty young partner. He turned back to me and held out *The Watchtower.*

"We'll just leave this," he said. "There may be other people in the house..."

I took *The Watchtower.* They left. If we'd had an ash pit, they'd have made the vicious dog mark.

A few years ago, our long-time friend Dr. Meyer Friedman, who died last year at 90, gave us a tape titled, *"The Culture of Complaint."* It's a talk by a Reverend Ortberg, and it deals with gratitude. It's a humorous talk, but it's also terribly serious. It has had a significant effect on me.

I'm still the same guy I was before I heard the tape, but I'm a more grateful guy. Now, when I wake up in the morning and look up at the tongue-and-groove boards in the ceiling, boards I've looked at for forty-some years, I feel a surge of gratitude.

It's undoubtedly helped by the fact I'll be old one of these days, and should simply be grateful I'm still around. Well, I do feel that, but I also I feel grateful I can see those boards overhead, see colors, smell smells, hear noises in the house. I can't walk as well as I would like, but I can do it well enough to get out to the kitchen where a great human being is already there, someone who will say good morning and give me a kiss and a cup of coffee.

It makes me echo Dr. Ortberg's words. "It's a *gift!*"

Before I get out of bed, therefore, I put my hands together, and even though I haven't the foggiest idea who I'm talking to, I say, "Thank you, God, for this day."

It *is* a gift. The whole day is a gift. Watching TV, reading a book, going to the supermarket, talking on the phone to one of our kids, it's a gift, plain and simple. How did I get so lucky?

I'm not Pollyanna. Bad stuff still happens. Do I ever feel like crying? Yes, but not a lot. Mostly, sitting in front of my computer writing this, or reading P.D. James, or watching "The Truman Show" one more time, or opening an envelope with a memoir in it, or some pictures from the Lake Mohonk weekend we missed, mostly it's a great big gift.

Well, boys and girls, that's my spiritual journey. Well, so far, anyhow. I had no idea it would take so long to get here from the ash pits of Denver. If you've followed me this far, that's another gift for which I am truly grateful.

I wrote a lot of stories while we were living in Sonoma. Many got sent to Willis Wing, who offered them to a broad spectrum of magazines. Some sold. A lot did not, and after making the rounds, came back to me. Others hung out with me in my converted dog kennel, unsent, awaiting something. Further revision? Confidence that they were ready to send to Willis?
I had some favorites among those that never made it into print. The Wonderful Leaf Collection *is one of them. I find it gratifying, so many years after its unsuccessful round trip to New York, that it's finding its way into print anyhow.*

The Wonderful Leaf Collection

"Where did you get it, Meg?" he asked. His voice, otherwise kindly, betrayed a faint edge of irritation. He had been lounging in his folding wooden chair, soaking up the warm rays of late spring sunshine. It was his favorite diversion of a fine Sunday afternoon, relaxing in this particular chair in this particular patch of sunshine while the pot roast and vegetables and roast potatoes worked contentedly in his stomach.

From Monday through Friday he was a patient bank teller. On Saturday he was a patient plumber, carpenter, housecleaner, or whatever else his wife Esther wanted him to be. On Sunday he was a monarch. On Sunday he divided his time between overeating and resting up from it.

His greatest dislike of a Sunday, therefore, was having to face any sort of problem, no matter how slight. Weekdays were for bank problems, and Saturday was for problems of house and home. Sunday was for contemplation. However, with his eight-year-old daughter now facing him, holding a twenty-dollar bill in her hand, he knew the day's contemplation was at an end.

"Where did you get it, Meg, dear?" he repeated. "Did Mommy give it to you?" He knew this was extremely unlikely; he seldom gave Esther as much as $20 at one time, and when he did, it was usually in ones and fives.

"Guess again, Father!" the child answered.

"Did you find it on my bureau?"

"No!"

"Well, then, where did you get it?"

The child's laughter tinkled brightly, like tiny triangular bits of glass suspended by strings, striking one another haphazardly in the breeze.

"You'll never guess!" she shouted happily, bounding up the back steps into the house. The teller leaned back in his chair and tried to recapture the serenity of his Sunday afternoon. The sun had a perfection found only when Spring heroically intrudes to confound the villainy of winter. It heated without causing perspiration. It soothed without burning. It relaxed the body without enervating. Yet, momentarily, its spell had been broken. The teller got up and walked to the base of the back steps.

"Is it play money?" he shouted into the house.

For answer he received a brilliant flutter of laughter, muffled and deflected by its passage through the maze of cluttered rooms and hallways.

The teller felt for his wallet. It rested where it should, buttoned securely into his left-hand back pocket, its concave side snuggled safely against the convexity of his tender buttock. The movement was more ritual than practical, for the teller made it a practice never to carry anything larger than a ten. The bill could not have come from his wallet.

Already the shade of the big oak that dominated the back yard was beginning to creep up the narrow wooden slats of the teller's folding footrest. It was time to move. He rose and pulled the chair noisily along the concrete slab he called the patio. Sitting down again, he tried to clear his mind, temporarily at least, of Meg's mysterious money.

"Emerson," his wife called from the top of the porch steps, "did you give this child a twenty-dollar bill?"

The teller opened his moist blue eyes. Dazzled by the sun, he turned and looked at his wife, shading his eyes with his hand.

"I did not," he replied. His voice admitted a certain amount of offended dignity. Did his wife think him so foolish as to give a child a large bill? "Did you, dear?" he countered.

"Ha!" said his wife mirthlessly. "Where would I see twenty dollars in one piece without visiting the mint?"

"Maybe she found it," the teller said. He sighed at his wife's increasingly frequent references to his parsimony. He had to be thrifty, what with the price of food and rent, and the cost of a decent insurance program in case anything happened to him. What he considered thrift, Esther considered penury. He sighed again and sank back in his chair.

It was no use. The chair was no longer a refuge. The slatted footrest cut his legs like a fakir's bed of nails. The sun was not hot enough. The breeze was too strong. The shade of the big oak tree was creeping toward him too fast. Inside his closed eyelids twenty-dollar bills fluttered like falling leaves. The child's laughter echoed through the convolutions of his ear canals, taunting, haunting him with a teller's distaste for an unidentified sum, a figure not accounted for, a digit out of balance. The folding chair creaked complainingly as he rose. He dusted the shiny, dustless rear of his blue serge trousers, and climbed the back steps to the house.

"I found it," the girl said. "I'm going to put it in my collection." She sat in the living room on the leather seat of a dark oak Morris chair. Her mother and father sat on the overstuffed borax sofa, facing her. The teller held the twenty dollar bill in his hand.

"You must tell us, Meg," he said. "Where did you find it?"

The girl jumped up and began to dance around the room, past the wheeled tea table that had been her great grandmother's, past the teller's walnut desk with its miniature fern garden and the glass bell jar that housed the stuffed canary. The silk tassels on the shades of the standing lamps shook with her merriment.

"That's the game," she shouted. "You have to guess!"

"This is a serious matter, Meg," said the teller, not unkindly for a man who has just discovered a crack in the perfection of his Sunday holiday. "You must tell us immediately where you found the bill."

Meg whirled about the room soundlessly, her gold hair flying and swirling about her face, her yellow cotton dress a spinning parasol, floating on air. The shepherd and his lass, supporting the ornate clock on the mantel above the gas log, stared at the silently pirouetting figure. Between this pastoral couple, enclosed in glass, a pendulum of four crystal shafts swung slowly back and forth, slicing infinitesimal segments from the lives of the quiet teller and his petulant wife and his fey daughter.

"Stop that nonsense," said the teller's wife, "and listen to your father. He wants to know where you found the bill."

"I found it in a tree," she said, whirling more slowly.

"Come now, Meg," said the teller. "Don't make us lose our patience. Where did you find it?"

"In a lovely tree," said Meg. "I was climbing in our beautiful oak tree, looking for fairies..."

"Fairies don't exist," her mother cut in. "You're too old for that."

"I was looking for them, all the same," the girl replied, "ever so high in the tree, when I saw the bill. At first I thought it was a wonderful leaf, and then I saw the picture on it, and the numbers and all, right where it was growing out of the tree. I'd never seen one growing on a tree before, so I picked it for my leaf collection. I pulled the stem off getting it down, but there's another in the tree. Next time I'm going to get it—stem and all!"

The lithe body wove its way through the furniture, and the childish voice sang a gay wordless song. A faint musty odor of ancient dust rose in the air.

"Meg," said the teller, "did you..." He paused. "Did you steal the money, Meg?"

The music stopped abruptly. The girl stood stockstill, staring at her father. There was no hint of indignation or resentment, merely surprise.

"I found it in the tree," she said. Then she disappeared through the half-opened sliding doors of the parlor into the dark recesses of the house.

The teller's pale blue eyes turned questioningly to his wife.

"I don't know what's come over Meg lately," said the woman. "She never used to make up stories. Emerson," she added, "I'm sure the child didn't steal it."

"Yes," said the teller, "I'm sorry I said it. She found it somewhere, that's certain. But Meg mustn't lie. She must be taught that lying, even in fun, is not a nice thing. Especially," he added, lapsing into his professional capacity as teller, "where money is concerned."

"Is this the tree, Meg?" the teller asked. The trio stood near the center of the backyard, where the huge serrated trunk of the oak sloped upward at a rakish angle from a neat circular hole in the cement. The oak was a tremendously powerful tree, a tree to be reckoned with, almost a druid tree. Already, in the two years since the teller had, over the span of four Saturdays, immersed half the backyard in concrete, the oak had showed its strength by the insouciance with which it fractured the paved squares. On its north and east sides the squares were cracked neatly in half, and the tree had raised the square on the south to such an angle that the teller had considered borrowing a sledge to break it up for removal.

Meg stood by her parents patiently, with an air of interrupted momentum.

"Yes, Father," she answered. "This is the tree."

"And you say there's another twenty-dollar bill growing from the limb where you found this one?"

The girl's brow clouded faintly. "I'm not absolutely certain it's a twenty, Father," she said. "I didn't look very carefully."

"But there is another bill, nevertheless," said the teller.

"Yes, Father."

"Would you get it for me, please, Meg?"

The girl nodded assent and began to climb the sloping trunk. When she reached the first jutting branch, she stopped and looked down. "Are you going to start a leaf collection, Father?" she asked hopefully.

"First you find the bill," the teller answered cordially. "Then I'll decide."

Meg's yellow dress disappeared into the high branches of the oak.

"I hope she will learn from this," said the teller, "that prevaricators are always discovered in their lies. To make the first twenty-dollar bill seem plausible, the child had to invent a second bill. Now she is forced to invent a new lie to explain why she comes down empty-handed. Lies breed lies. Meg will see it. She's a smart girl."

"Then maybe she will tell us where the first bill came from," Esther said.

The couple looked up in the tree. The foliage obscured Meg's figure completely. The teller chuckled. "In a way this is amusing," he said. Cupping his hands around his mouth, he shouted upwards. "Meg, have you found it?"

Meg's voice shimmered down from the treetop.

"Not yet, Father," it said. The teller chuckled to himself.

Meg stayed hidden from view for five minutes. "If you can't find it," her father shouted, "come on down."

"Coming," Meg said. Out of the foliage came a foot, a leg, the brief yellow cotton dress, finally the whole delicate body. Meg scrambled down to the ground. Her hands were empty.

"Well," said the teller, smiling ever so gently, "did you find it?"

Meg turned her back, lifted the front of her dress, and reached inside the waistband of her underpants. "Here it is, Father," she said. "It *was* a twenty, after all."

The teller's smile vanished. "Meg, did you hide this bill up there?" His voice had an incipient edge of severity, the sound of a man who had been trifled with long enough.

"No, Father," Meg said, bewildered at his tone.

"Did you carry it up the tree in your underpants?"

"No, Father."

"Then how did it get there?" the teller demanded.

"I told you, Father," Meg said innocently. "It just grew, like a leaf."

"That's enough, Meg!" said her mother. "Don't irritate your father any more. We all know money doesn't grow on trees!"

"But, Mother..." Meg protested.

"You'd better go to your room, Meg," said the teller, "until you're ready to tell us where the money came from."

"They look like genuine Federal Reserve notes," the teller said. He sat at the large walnut desk by the front window. In his right hand he held a large bone-handled magnifying glass, through which he was squinting painstakingly at the two bills. He offered the magnifying glass to his wife. "Here, do you want a look?"

"No, thanks," said his wife. "I wouldn't know a counterfeit if it said 'counterfeit' right on it."

"Every citizen, Esther," said the teller, "should know the rudiments of how to identify counterfeit currency. Now, the first thing is to look for the small, colored hairs in the paper itself. If the bill is genuine..."

"Don't bother," Esther interrupted. "I don't see enough money to make it worth my while knowing."

The teller sighed and put the magnifying glass back in the desk drawer.

"I think it's all rather simple," he said. "She found a wallet or a roll of bills in the street, and she hid it in the tree. Now she's having a joke on us by bringing them down one by one."

"How much do you suppose she has up there?"

"I don't know, " the teller said, "but I think I'll find out."

"Be careful, Emerson," said the teller's wife. "You've never climbed a tree before."

"Of course I've climbed trees before," said the teller. "Don't you think I had a childhood?"

The teller had waited until dark in order to climb unobserved.

He wore a pair of gray wool pants that had once been part of his best suit, a shirt from which the collar had been detached, and a pair of high lace-up tennis shoes left over from his high-school days. A flashlight protruded from his back pocket.

"You've put on plenty of weight since you wore that suit," his wife observed.

"The trousers were always tight," the teller said.

Having his midsection pulled in so firmly made him feel very athletic. He leaned forward, let his arms dangle loosely, and shook them violently.

"What's that for?" Esther asked.

"Loosens the muscles," he answered haughtily. "Well, here goes!" He walked stealthily across the back porch and started down the stairs. When he felt he had reached the bottom, he stepped forward confidently into the dark patio. His foot stabbed through the air, doubled under him. He lurched forward into an ungainly heap, and the flashlight clattered from his pocket to the cement, rolling toward the oak tree. He had miscounted.

"Are you all right, Emerson?" Esther called from the porch.

"Sh-h-h-h," said the teller, clutching his ankle. When he had rubbed it for several minutes, he crept forward on his hands and knees, searching for the flashlight.

Emerson Wilmot's ascent of the oak tree was not an accomplished performance. He found the bare-bark climb to the first limb more of a feat than it seemed when Meg scampered up. Nevertheless he climbed carefully and steadily, always finding a handhold when he needed it and a branch to support his feet. He skinned his knuckles badly moving about some of the upper branches, but he did his job with persistence and thoroughness. As he approached each limb, he shone the flashlight along the bottom side of it, and as he gained a seat on the limb, he shone the light along the top and sides. From time to time he heard a screen door slam. He was glad Meg's room was on the front of the house, for he preferred she know nothing about his investigation.

The teller was in the tree an hour and three-quarters in all. He was ready to come down, empty-handed, when he heard a male voice from the base of the tree.

"Hey, Tarzan!"

The teller switched off his light and sat very still.

"Hey, Wilmot, is that you up this tree?"

The teller cleared his throat.

"Wilmot, is that you?"

"It is I," the teller said.

"What are you doing?"

Slowly and carefully, without answering, the teller climbed down to the cement where Julius Jackson, his next-door neighbor, stood watching.

"What you got up there?" Jackson asked. "A girl?"

"Oh, it's you, Jackson," said the teller.

"What you doing up in the tree?"

'The teller coughed rhetorically. "Well," he said, "I was conducting a sort of investigation."

"What sort of investigation can you conduct in a tree?" Jackson asked.

"I was making sure the tree isn't diseased. It's very old, you know."

"Diseased?" Jackson queried.

"There's a lot of Dutch Elm Blight around," said the teller.

"But this here's an oak tree!"

The teller's voice began to show annoyance. "That's why I'm particularly anxious not to have it contract the disease," he said. "Once the oaks are involved, we might as well surrender all our trees!"

"But why at night, Wilmot?" Jackson asked. "Seems to me I saw you sitting over here on your rusty-dusty most of the afternoon when you could have been tree-climbing in daylight."

"That's true," said the teller. "I didn't want to alarm the neighbors about The Blight if there was no danger of the local trees becoming involved."

"Look, Wilmot, next time you want to save me from being alarmed, just call me up and tell me straight, instead of poking around in a tree with a flashlight. I was about to call the police."

"Oh, no," said the teller, retreating toward the house, "there's no need to call the police."

During his lunch hour on Monday Emerson deposited the two twenty-dollar bills in his account at the Midland Bank. He had never kept an account at the First National, where he worked, because he didn't want his fellow workers nosing around, looking at his balance. After the deposit, the balance looked slightly higher than he had a right to expect this early in the week, so he wrote a check and withdrew ten dollars. On Thursday night he took Esther and Meg to dinner and the movies. It was a gay party, and there was enough money left from the ten for Emerson to buy several long Havana cigars, the type that bankers are reputed to smoke.

"Meg, I want to talk to you," the teller said. It was the following Saturday morning, and the Wilmots had just finished breakfast.

"Yes, Father?"

"Meg, I haven't pestered you about those bills you said you found in the tree last week, have I?"

"No, Father."

"And I took you to dinner and the movies this week, so you know I'm not holding anything against you, don't you, Meg?"

"Yes, Father."

"Then are you ready to tell me where you got the bills? I promise I won't be angry."

"I told you once, Father," Meg said, "but you were angry."

"I know, Meg. I'm sorry. Now, do you suppose you could find more bills if you climbed the tree again?"

"Oh, yes, Father! I know I could!"

"How do you know?"

"Well..." Meg hesitated.

"Go on," said Emerson. "I won't make any fuss."

"Well," Meg said. "I ... well, I got some more out of the tree yesterday."

"May I see them?"

Meg lifted the dress front and reached inside the waistband of the underpants. She unfolded and laid three bills on the kitchen table, a fifty-dollar bill and two singles.

The teller examined them carefully. "Was this all you saw?" he asked.

"Oh, no, Father," Meg said. "But these had the best stems. I picked them for my collection."

"I don't see any stems."

"The stems came off," Meg said. "No matter how careful I am, they always seem to come off before I get them to the ground."

"Meg," said the teller, "would you do me a favor? Would you climb the tree now, please, and bring me down as many bills as you can find?"

Emerson Wilmot sat on the back porch in his ancient flannel bathrobe drinking coffee while Meg foraged in the tree above. As the sun rose higher, he went indoors and returned with a pair of dark glasses and a fresh cup of coffee. A screen door slammed nearby.

"Hello, Jungle Jim," Jackson said across the fence. "I see you've got Meg investigating the Elm Blight today."

Wilmot cleared his throat ominously.

"Okay, okay," said Jackson. "I'm not alarmed."

"Twelve fifties, five twenties, two tens, eleven ones," the teller said. "That's $731. That's all you saw?"

"There were some little ones," Meg said, "but I didn't think I ought to pick them."

"What denomination?"

"What what?"

"How big?"

"Oh, about two or three inches, I guess."

"No," said Wilmot, "I mean were they twenties or fifties or what?"

"I didn't even notice," Meg said. "They were too small to

pick."

Wilmot added the $731 to his account at the Midland Bank the following Monday noon. He brought a dozen carnations home to Esther on Tuesday, and on Thursday he took Esther and Meg to the Curry & Wheems Circus. They each had a front-row box seat at $2.65 apiece, even Meg, who was only eight years old and should have gone half-price.

The following Saturday Wilmot kept Meg busy most of the morning. He sent her into the oak tree right after breakfast with instructions to check each branch carefully, pick all the bills that were the right size, and not to miss a trick. She came down with four one-hundred-dollar bills, seven fifties, six twenties, and a one. This totaled $871. Wilmot sent Meg up once more just to check, to make sure she hadn't missed anything. Meg came down with two more bills, a fifty and a single, and the total for the day swelled to $922.

On Sunday morning Wilmot again sent Meg into the oak tree.

"They don't grow much in a day," Meg said.

Wilmot deposited the $922 in his Midland account on Monday. Tuesday afternoon an express truck delivered Meg's bicycle, packed in a heavy cardboard box. Meg loved it so much she was almost reluctant to stop riding and accompany her parents to dinner at the Mayfair, and to the double-feature afterwards.

"I see the Wilmots have a new car," said Helen Jackson.

"It ain't new..." Julius said. "It's two years old."

"It looks new..." said his wife.

"Well, it ain't."

"Who cares? It's a car," Helen said.

"I wouldn't have a Pontiac," her husband said, "if you gave it to me!"

"That's the only way we'll ever get one," Helen answered, with a drop of bitterness.

"We could have a better car than that," said Julius, "only I don't want to put myself in hock to some finance company."

"Emerson Wilmot paid cash."

"Who says?"

"Sarah Hopkins. She got it from Anna Fragle, who is a good friend of Esther Wilmot's sister-in-law."

"I don't know where he gets it," Julius said. "Emerson Wilmot don't make a cent more than me even if he does work in a bank."

"Mr. Davis is here to see you, sir. He says it's urgent."

The bank president's carefully manicured right hand pressed the lever on his intercom. A red light went on. "Send him in." The massive office door, veneered in Philippine mahogany to match the paneled walls, swung open. Davis, the second youngest vice-president in the history of the First National, came in.

"Is that thing turned off, sir?" he inquired, pointing to the intercom. The president flipped a switch and turned back to Davis.

"It's the auditors, sir," Davis said. "I'm afraid they've got hold of something."

The president frowned.

"I thought we ought to talk it over immediately," Davis continued, "so we can figure out what to say when the press finds out."

"What have they found?"

"There's been some pretty fancy juggling in the books, apparently, and $39,500 is missing."

"In whose department?" the president asked.

"In Paying and Receiving, N-to-Z. I've been working on it for the past hour, ever since they told me, and I've narrowed it down to two possibilities. I feel certain that the juggling was done either by Henry Tanner or Emerson Wilmot."

"Emerson, darling," Esther said. She had just had a shampoo, a facial, and a permanent. Her brown hair was several shades lighter, and her fingernails matched her lipstick. "It's the most beautiful coat I've ever seen. Who ever dreamed I'd have a coat trimmed in genuine mink!"

"I'm glad you like it," Emerson said. "I think I'll get one just like it for Meg. The man at the store suggested it. 'Look-alikes' they call it."

"It's like a dream," Esther said, "the way the tree has changed our lives. I feel different, I look different—I even think differently now."

"I've been thinking, too," Emerson said, "thinking ahead. Maybe we ought to make a down-payment on a house of our own, instead of renting for the rest of our lives."

"Oh, Emerson!"

"There's only one hitch—the tree. Naturally we couldn't take it with us. Without it, we couldn't pay for the house. In fact, without the tree we'd be right back where we started."

"Maybe we could buy this house," Esther suggested.

"I thought of that," Emerson said, "but on the other hand, maybe it's time we moved into a better class neighborhood and got away from barbarians like that Jackson."

Esther looked thoughtful. "I suppose you're right," she said, "but there's the tree..."

"Ah, yes, Wilmot," said Mr. Watson, the bank president, "Sit down, won't you?" Mr. Watson had just come from the barber, and his silver gray hair had a faint touch of bluing in it. As he motioned the teller to a chair, his coat fell open slightly, though certainly not enough for anyone to see the label identifying it as a custom garment from the exclusive salon of Arthur Seidel, Tailors to Gentlemen.

The knowledge that his grooming was faultless gave Watson a feeling of confidence when he faced people, particularly people who patronized barbershops solely for haircuts and bought their clothing off the hook. He was therefore mildly dismayed to notice that Emerson Wilmot's gray hair had something of a blue-silver cast to it, not unlike his own, and that Wilmot's charcoal-gray suit fitted uncommonly well.

"I expect you know why you're here, Wilmot," said the bank president. He leaned back in his deep leather swivel chair and pressed his fingertips together.

"I'm afraid not, sir," said the teller.

The bank president swung his chair around until he faced the large window at the side of his office. "No idea, eh?"

Wilmot's liquid blue eyes focussed on the marble pen-and-pencil set on the president's desk. He was slow to answer.

"Well, just a little one, sir," he said.

Watson swung back and glared at Wilmot. "What is it?"

"I'd rather not say, sir," Wilmot said. "It might sound presumptuous."

Two wrinkles of anger appeared at the corners of the bank president's mouth. His eyes narrowed.

"That's a nice looking suit you have on, Wilmot," he said.

"Thank you, sir."

"It must have cost you quite a bit."

"Yes, sir, it did," Wilmot said. With a touch of pride he added, "It's tailor-made. To my measurements."

"How much did it cost?"

"One hundred and seventy-five dollars."

"Do you own a car, Wilmot?"

"Yes, sir."

"Is it paid for?"

"Yes, sir."

"What model is it?"

"It's a Buick, sir, a new Buick sedan."

"Where do you bank, Wilmot?"

"At the Midland."

"What is your balance at present?"

Wilmot paused. His hand reached inside his coat and withdrew a brown-paper-covered notebook. He flipped it open, and for a moment the blue eyes scanned the ruled page. Then he looked up. "Do I have to tell, sir?"

"No, you don't," the president thundered, "because I can tell you to the exact penny! As of one hour ago it was $33,421.09! That's what it is! And it has all been deposited during the past five months, during the same period when the books of this bank turned up $39,500 short! Now, Wilmot, if you can put two and two together, you have some idea why I have called you in today!" Angrily he pressed a buzzer. The outside door opened, and two men in blue uniforms stepped inside.

"I'm going to give you some fatherly advice, Wilmot," Watson said, "before these men take you away. I'm going to advise you to plead guilty. I am told by our lawyers that your chances for drawing a light sentence will be improved immeasurably if you do. You've had a good record with us, Wilmot, up to now, and the bank is not eager to see an old employee spend the rest of his days in prison, even though he has made a grievous mistake."

Wilmot stood up. His eyes were open wide. He stared aghast at Watson, then at the two policemen near the door. He fumbled as he replaced the brown notebook in his coat pocket. When he spoke, his voice sounded hollow and far away.

"You've made a mistake, Mr. Watson," he said. "I've done nothing wrong."

"Then where did you get $33,000 and new cars and new clothes in the short space of five months?"

There were more people in the office now. Davis and two other vice-presidents stood near the bluecoats. An aging, golden blonde secretary with deep circles under her eyes came in through the side door. Another policeman pushed in through the main door. Wilmot's stricken eyes took them in, one by one. Finally he turned to the bank president.

"Mr. Watson," he said. "I've been with this bank for more than 17 years. For fourteen of them I've been a teller, standing behind the brass wicket of the N-to-Z Paying-and-Receiving window, counting out money, stamping checks, correcting the addition on deposit slips, trying to deal with the bank's customers in a helpful, cheerful way. Seventeen years is a long time, Mr.

Watson, not a lifetime, but when it's carved from the heart of a lifetime it might as well be the whole life.

"Every year I've seen younger men come into the bank, spend a year or two as a teller, and then pass by me on their way up the ladder. Maybe they were better tellers than I was, Mr. Watson, but I don't know. It was I who had to teach them what to do, how to look for the error in their day's end balance, teach them how and where and when. And then it was I who had to shake their hands and congratulate them on their promotions and, in a couple more years, start calling them 'sir' when they came by my cage.

"You asked me if I had any idea why you'd called me in, Mr. Watson, and I said I had a little one, but I wouldn't say what it was. Well, I'll tell you now. I thought maybe the bank had seen fit to—well, to give me more responsibility, to promote me after seventeen years of loyal service. I thought maybe you were going to say 'Wilmot, how would you like to become a loan officer?' or, 'Wilmot, the job of head teller is open, what do you say?'

"But now I know what it was that you wanted. You wanted to tell me that the bank is short some money, and you think I took it. Well, I have only one thing to say, Mr. Watson. For seventeen-odd years—up to today, in fact—the bank has believed me, and now I'm going to ask it to believe me one more time. I swear to God I did not take this or any other money from the bank. The money I have in my Midland account—well, Mr. Watson, I know it's hard to believe, but it grew on a tree in my backyard!"

Watson stared at Wilmot with troubled eyes. "I'm sorry to do this, Emerson," he said. He nodded to the policemen. "I ask that you arrest this man for embezzling the funds of the First National Bank." He turned to Davis. "After he's booked, Howard, see that he gets bail."

Autumn winds and swirling leaves came early, and the trial was postponed until mid-November. Meg fell from the old oak tree, clutching $617 in fifties, twenties, fives and ones, the weekend after the bank suspended Wilmot. The cast on her left arm now prevented her from climbing the tree in search of any more greenbacks. Wilmot climbed the tree twice more, but he found nothing other than small acorns and browning leaves, almost ready to drop.

Since Wilmot's account at the Midland had been attached, pending the trial, he was forced to sell the Buick to pay the rent and keep food in the house. Esther kept the mink-trimmed coat, but the beauty treatments ceased, and her hair grew out to the point where it was obvious that the light color was not indigenous. Two or three days a week Emerson went out to look for work, but no one would take on a man accused of being an embezzler.

On top of everything else, the landlord made his semiannual visit. The landlord decided that the oak tree was leaning to the south so radically that it constituted a danger to the adjacent buildings, which he also owned. He would therefore send a crew to take it down.

Emerson argued vehemently against the removal. "It's the only bit of beauty left in the block," he said.

"Fine bit of beauty if it falls and conks someone on the head," said the landlord. "Fine damage suit, if you ask me!"

Emerson fingered the frayed cuff of his flannel bathrobe as he sat in his folding chair on the back porch and watched the men work. Limb by limb they lowered the old tree and carried it through the side yard to the waiting trucks. The air smelled of hot sawdust tinged with gasoline from the motors of the chain saws. From time to time Emerson touched his lips with a cup of bitter coffee, but it had been cold almost since he sat down. Meg sat beside him most of the morning, watching. At noon, when the workmen knocked off for lunch, she went down and wandered among the sawn branches with a bucket.

At 4:15, when the job was almost finished, a long, black limousine pulled up in front of Wilmot's house. A gray-clad figure in a homburg climbed to the front stoop, rang, and entered. A moment later he stood beside Emerson on the back porch.

"I don't know quite how to say it," the figure began.

Wilmot looked up. He rose. "Hello, Mr. Watson," he said. "I guess there isn't much to say until the trial, is there?"

"We've wronged you, Emerson," Mr. Watson said. "We've done you a grave injustice. I should have known you'd never do such a thing. We caught Tanner red-handed at 2:30 this afternoon. He walked out of the bank with some marked bills. Confessed everything."

"Emerson, I offer you my sincere personal apology as well as that of the bank."

Emerson looked thoughtfully at the stump rising from the cement circle in the middle of the backyard.

"Oh," he said. "Oh. That's all right."

"Naturally, we have vacated the attachment on your Midland account, and we will see to it that any other damage or injustice wrought through our error is rectified."

He paused and cleared his throat.

"One more thing, Emerson," he said, "the job of head teller happens to be open at the present moment. I wonder if we could prevail on you to accept the position—at a considerably higher salary, of course, retroactive to the day we committed our wrong. You can think it over and let me know when you come in Monday."

Emerson followed the workman who carried the last limb out to the street, and shut the side-yard gate behind him.

"Well, take it easy," said the workman, starting up the engine of his truck.

Wilmot raised his hand in a brief acknowledgement. The truck started with a jerk. The tree-limbs shook. A shower of leaves fell into the gutter. Wilmot leaned over and picked a five-dollar bill from the middle of the heap.

"Look at my acorn!" Meg announced from the front stoop. "I split it open with a kitchen knife."

"That's nice, Meg," Wilmot said absently.

"Did you ever see the insides of an acorn?" Meg asked.

She ran to Wilmot's side and deposited the acorn in his hand. Its tough skin was split neatly into two leathery hemispheres. Inside the skin lay a large yellow pellet.

As Wilmot examined it, his brows came together in an attitude of concentration.

"Heavy, isn't it," Meg said.

Wilmot tossed the half-opened acorn up and down in his hand judgmentally. "Almost like gold," he said. "Where did you get it, Meg?"

"I got a bushel basket full," Meg answered, "before they took the old oak." She turned her face up to her father, her eyes aglow with enthusiasm.

"Let's start a collection, shall we?" she said.

Arthur Henry Louis Rissman
1920-1998

Arthur

Arthur's son called three nights ago, at 10:30.

"Arthur left us this morning," he said.

He apologized for calling late. He invited my wife and me to a service at Arthur's house in Mill Valley. "We'll have a rabbi, a Zen priest, and then we'll have a potluck party and talk about Arthur. He'd like that."

Arthur and I had met long ago in a business context. We had liked one another, met socially for some years, then dropped out of touch. Now, we were back in touch.

Mill Valley is Mill Valley, a journey back in time, and Arthur is Arthur, another journey back to the heady days of group introspection and transactional analysis.

Friends bearing food poured into Arthur's spare, simple house. We ate, sipped wine, and talked. We leafed through a welter of photographs covering a large, rectangular table in the living room. Young Arthur, coated and tied, smiling with his graduating class from Hebrew academy. Arthur the businessman, smiling suavely as he introduced Sir Somebody to a kilted child. Arthur the teacher, a paint-splattered smock partially covering his crisp, pristine linen and carefully-tied Ascot, smiling as he explained chiaroscuro.

This was Arthur before I had met him. Arthur with his wife, his children. Arthur at home, at the beach, a youthful Arthur, clean-shaven, stylish, smiling. I recognized the later pictures—

Arthur, the sage, the counselor, the earnest lecturer. Arthur, the small, immaculate cherub with the handsome white beard and the twinkle.

The rabbi began a plaintive tune on a wooden flute. He was tall, slender, weathered. He wore faded, blue cotton trousers, blue shirt, a blue, knitted yarmulke. He could have been a mariner just off a barque from Haifa.

The rabbi knew Arthur well. Arthur attended services. Sometimes. But Arthur was also a Buddhist, the rabbi said. And Arthur had adopted bits of Christianity, and other beliefs as well. The rabbi spoke of the Jewish belief in the eternity of things. He spoke of the Law of Conservation of Energy. No energy is ever lost, none can be added.

"Arthur is with us somewhere," the rabbi said. "We just don't know where."

When they would meet, the rabbi said, Arthur would beam, "Hello, rabbi! You know, I'm a rabbi, too! I'm a teacher, I'm a part of God. And over there, look, there's the tree rabbi. And the dog rabbi. And the sky rabbi."

Unexpectedly, Arthur's view resonated within me. I don't reject the God of Moses or of Jesus, or of anyone else. I just feel that, whatever God there is, I'm a part of him. Just like the dog rabbi and the tree rabbi and the sky rabbi.

Walking on the fire trail near our home, I see the occasional deer, and I have been warned about the occasional mountain lion. In forty years I've never seen one. What I do see lots of, however, are lizards and snakes, beetles and butterflies.

The butterflies especially get my attention. They fly ahead of me, light on the trail, take off as I approach, land in front of me again. They accompany me like an old, faithful dog. Until I walked the fire trail I never thought much about transmigration, but now I find myself wondering: Are these my father and mother? Are they other bygone friends? Or are they just butterflies?

Sometimes, in the middle of the night, I ask myself a similar question. I wake up, it's still dark. I look at my liquid-crystal alarm clock. The glowing red numbers say: 4:57. Why, that's our old number on High Street! That's where I was born, the house where my parents lived for 65 years. Are my parents trying to get my attention? If so, they've certainly succeeded!

Then I wonder: When I think of them, do they know it? Does it make them feel good? Is this how it works? Is there a device "on their side" that keeps track of the times I think of them? Is there a counter counting "hits" at their website?

Yesterday, I saw a snake on the fire trail. About three feet long, tan with large, brown spots. Idly, I thought, "Anyone I know?"

There were the usual butterflies—brown, unspectacular, but always friendly. Then I saw a butterfly I'd never seen before. It was tiny. It had a wingspread smaller than a dime. It was a beautiful blue, powder blue, elegant and extremely active.

"Arthur!" I thought.

If it wasn't Arthur, it was a "hit" on Arthur's celestial website. It made me think of him, and see him, impeccably togged, cheerfully busy, setting about his day's work.

At the very least, it was the butterfly rabbi.

Heat Lightning

That summer after Mama died, we had lots of hot, still nights full of heat lightning, and no rain. We used to sit in the swing on the front porch and watch it, Weena and me, in our scratchy muslin dresses, with Gram rocking just inside the front window, and the shades drawn. Gram didn't like the lightning.

"What is it, Blue?" Weena would ask, moving closer, while the swing creaked and the air, motionless and hot, camped on the porch with us, just as though it were another person. When the lightning flashed, we could see the whole front yard. It was just plain dirt, but at night I used to pretend it was grass. All around the horizon the sheets of light kept flickering and flashing—over the fields straight ahead, and off toward Jefferson to the right, and off to the left, toward town.

"It's just heat lightning, Weena," I would say. "Nothing to be scared of."

"I don't like it," Weena would say, moving closer and clutching what was left of her old string doll. She thought Daddy had sent it to her. She called it Boo-wah.

"Boo-wah doesn't like it, either," she'd say.

The light would flash again, noiselessly, and Weena would hide her eyes. Inside, behind the drawn curtain, Gram's rocker would creak back and forth, back and forth, until finally she'd call out, "Blue! Rowena! Why aren't you in bed?"

All that summer there was heat lightning and no rain. One night, after we'd gone to bed, Weena asked me, "Where do people come from?"

"What kind of people?" I said.

"Oh, just people," she said.

"They come from other people," I said.

"What other people?" she said.

"Just other people," I said. Someday I was going to tell Weena where people came from, because I knew. But not till she was at least ten, like me.

On the seventeenth of July that summer a package came for

Weena and me from the Philippine Islands. It wasn't tied very well, and it didn't say who sent it. It had little carved wooden statues in it—four of them. Three of them were broken. The other one was my favorite right away. Weena's, too. It was a man pulling a thing Gram said was a ricka-shaw.

"They're from Daddy," I said.

"I doubt it," Gram said.

"I'm sure they are," I said. I didn't remember Daddy any too well, but I knew he'd sent them. "Or else who did, then?" I said.

"God knows," Gram said. "If it was your father, it's the first thing he ever sent!"

"He sent Boo-wah," Weena said.

Gram picked up the ricka-shaw and looked at it hard and set it down again. "Oh, he did, did he?" she said.

In the fall of that year, when Mama had been dead nine months, and Weena was six, Gram took us all the way to Norfolk, Virginia, to visit her sister who was my great-aunt. One day Gram took us down to the water to see the ships go by. They were big ships, long and gray and beautiful, with big numbers painted on the side up near the front.

"They're going to war," Gram said.

"Is Daddy on one of them?" I asked her.

"I don't know," Gram said.

"He's in the Navy still, isn't he?" I said.

Gram didn't answer. She just set her chin a little harder, and looked at the silent, gray ships sliding past with the little colored flags flying and flapping in the wind.

Weena was sitting in the sand beside us, playing with Boo-wah. Boo-wah was just a tangle of strings by then.

"Isn't he, Gram?" I said. "Isn't he in the Navy still?"

"Yes," Gram said finally. "In the brig probably."

"What's a brig?" I said, and when Gram didn't answer, I said, "Do you ever hear from him?"

Gram sucked in a big breath and let it out. "Sometimes," she said.

"What does he say?" I said. "Does he ask about Weena and me?"

Gram kept looking out at the ships. "Mostly he just sends a check," she said.

"He sends money?" I said. "Money to take care of us?"

"They make him," Gram said.

Gram thought Daddy had killed Mama. Mama had been Gram's little girl, just like Weena and I were Mama's. Gram said this thing about killing Mama when we got back to my great-aunt's house that night. Not to Weena she didn't say it, just to me.

"But he couldn't have!" I said.

"Not the way you're thinking," Gram said, sticking her needle through the heel of one of my socks that was stretched tight around her darning egg.

"Then how?" I said.

"Do you know John Barleycorn?" Gram said, stabbing at the sock as though it were her enemy.

"No," I said. "Who is he?"

"He's a friend of your father's," Gram said. "He's the one who killed her."

I shook my head. "John Barleycorn killed Mama?" I said.

Gram took a big breath and looked at me. "Well, to start with your Ma was real sick," she said. "Real sick."

She said it like she was going to tell me some more. But she didn't. Instead, she turned and looked out the front window. It was black out there. You couldn't see anything.

Then she looked at the clock.

"Eight o'clock!" she said. "Why aren't you in bed?"

Weena took sick that winter after we got home from Norfolk. Gram said it was just a cold, but later on she called old Dr. Evans. He came in every morning for a little while, and again every afternoon, until one afternoon he came in and just stayed.

They didn't let me see Weena that day, and I didn't have to go to bed when it was eight o'clock, either. No one paid much attention to me until awful late, and then they asked if I wanted to say good night to Weena.

I went in, and Weena was lying in Gram's big bed, with the covers pulled up to her chest and her hands lying where the sheet turned back over the blanket. I'd never seen her look so little before.

I just stood there and looked at her, and after a while I said, "Good night, Weena."

At first I didn't think she heard me. Then her tongue came out a little way and tried to lick her lips, and she said, "I want Boo-wah."

I ran out of the room and looked all around for Boo-wah, but I couldn't find him. I kept looking and looking, and finally there he was, under the dining room table where Weena and I had been playing house before she took sick. I picked him up and ran back up the stairs to the room where Weena was, but they wouldn't let me in any more.

I hardly remember the funeral, except that I cried an awful lot. Not loud, though, not the way you do when you fall down. Someone sent about a million yellow roses, without a card or anything. It made Gram mad.

"Who ever heard of yellow roses at a funeral?" she said when we got home and were taking off our black clothes.

Without Weena it was awful lonesome around the house. Some days I didn't know what to do. I tried playing with Boo-wah, even though I was getting kind of old for dolls, especially one that was just a bunch of dirty string. I spent a lot of time looking at the wooden ricka-shaw man.

Every now and then Gram talked about the war that was on. It was us against evil, Gram said, and every night she made me pray that God would strike down the enemy. The war didn't mean much to me, except that Gram was extra strict about how much sugar I used, and we stopped having butter.

And then one day Gram got a telegram. She wouldn't tell me what it said. Time kept on passing by until it was summer again, and hot, and one night I was sitting on the porch when a man in a beautiful Navy uniform with gold stripes came by to see Gram. They talked in the front parlor for almost an hour. I couldn't hear much, except Gram said something about nothing public. I just sat there in the heavy air, swinging a little, and when the man was through talking to Gram, he came out on the porch.

I stood up, and he looked at me, straight in the eyes, and smiled. He held out his hand and took mine and shook it, and held it for a minute. He said, "God bless you, little lady." Then he stood up straight and put his hand up to his hat and saluted.

After he'd gone, Gram called me inside and handed me a little box. "Here, this is for you, Blue," she said.

It was a blue box, dark blue, and the top opened and shut on a hinge. The inside was lined with white silk, and there was a beautiful ribbon pinned to it, with a sort of medal attached. The ribbon was blue with a white stripe down the middle, and the medal was a cross.

"It's beautiful, Gram," I said. "Where did it come from?"

For a minute Gram didn't say anything. Finally, she said, "It's from your father."

"He sent it to me?" I said.

Gram took a long time to answer. "Yes," she said finally. "He sent it to you, Blue. I'll explain all about it tomorrow. Now, you run along to bed."

Gram went upstairs without even turning off her reading light, but I didn't follow her. I took Daddy's badge out of the box and pinned it on my dress, and then I went out on the porch again and sat down in the swing.

I sat there till nearly midnight, swinging, and thinking about the medal Daddy had sent. And then after a while I thought about Weena, and how she never found out where people come from.

William Porter Nelson, II
1917-2000

My Brother Porter

Church of the Ascension,
Denver, Colorado, September 24, 2000

It's been a long time since Porter and I first came to Ascension in our best blue suits, mine with short pants, his with knickers. So it's fitting that we should come here again today, in flesh and spirit, to celebrate his life.

The Church of the Ascension was an important part of both our lives. We walked up here together every Sunday. Well, "together" may be too strong a word. Porter would be striding along ahead, eager to meet his friends, and I would be scrambling along behind, yelling, "Hey, wait for me!"

When Porter became an altar boy, I wanted to become one, too. And in the fullness of time, I did. I wasn't as good a one as Porter, however, because, kneeling in my vestments at 7:30 Communion on Saturday mornings, on an empty stomach—can't eat anything before Communion, you know—I had a tendency to pass out. I'd wake up flat on the floor with Father Wolcott pouring holy water over my temples.

At times like these, I was kind of sorry Porter had become an altar boy. Because, if he hadn't, I wouldn't have, either.

For me, Porter was a trailblazer. I don't just mean being an altar boy and that kind of thing, and I don't mean the kinds of trails he blazed in getting the National Arthritis Act passed and signed. I mean, he blazed trails by being born four years earlier than I, and, therefore, being responsible for the training of our parents.

Even though we had exceptional parents—intelligent, responsive, quick to learn—it was no picnic for Porter to break them in. But he did it, and I was the beneficiary.

I think, in fact, Porter occasionally succeeded a little better than he might have wished. He was nearly 11 years old before he could wheedle a bicycle out of Mother and Dad, but thanks to his pioneer work, I got mine at nine. The same was true with our Lionel electric trains, a two-year difference. The same was true with the age at which each of us was allowed to walk down to the Hiawatha Theater on Saturday to spend our dime on seeing a newsreel, a cartoon, a short subject, a chapter of the current serial, and the feature movie.

Porter never complained about this disparity, at least not very much. And I don't suppose I was very grateful to him at the time. But I'm grateful to him now. It's the kind of recognition that doesn't come to you until you get older, and have children of your own, and the first child has to train you.

Marie-Louise, Jeffrey, Rebecca—be grateful to your big brother Jamie, who did for you what my brother Porter did for me.

Little brothers are a pain, especially if they want to tag along with the older kids. That's what I wanted to do, tag along with Porter and Ben Stapleton and Bill Beggs. For a brief period Porter gave me a nickname—"Tagalong"—but it didn't last. Porter never really minded my tagging along too terribly, and I got to play endless games of Monopoly and Battleship and Capture the Flag and poker with "the big kids."

I learned a lot from those kids, and I learned a lot when Porter went to high school, and his friends would stop by in the afternoon, or on Saturday, or come to dinner. Colin James, Shelton Doyle, a lot of great guys, I looked up to all of them. They were kind of extensions of Porter. You could absorb a lot sitting around a dining room table, listening to them while you ate our mother's great lamb roast and our father's great Meadow Gold Ice Cream, freshly made that same day down at the dairy where Dad worked.

Porter and his friends played chess, and I learned to play chess. They played tennis, and I learned to play tennis. They were in the Congress Debating Society at East Denver High School, and when I got to East Denver High School I played tennis and chess and debated Friday nights just the way they all had four years earlier.

I was still in junior high, though, when Porter entered the University of Denver, and pledged Beta Theta Pi. I thought the whole thing was wonderful. To continue mirroring Porter's pathway through life, I founded, along with Bobby Hover, whose brother was also a pledge, the Beta Theta Pi Little Brothers Club. Bobby and I learned the Greek alphabet, and we learned all the stupid things the pledges had to say when, for example, an "active" asked them what time it was.

I can remember it now.

"Sire, although my chronometer is not in precise alignment with the great celestial movements over which I have no control, I beg to say, without fear of being totally inaccurate, that the correct time is...twenty-three minutes after four o'clock, Sire!"

Something like that. I could say it better than Bobby. It was a two-man club, and Bobby's heart wasn't in it the way mine was.

I went to college vicariously through Porter. I got excited when the Betas staged their annual chariot race with the Alpha Sigs. I went out to watch Porter play tennis for the University when he was captain of the team. I was baffled and envious when he talked about the "Rat House," an experimental lab at the University where he and a lot of people who sounded very intriguing spent a lot of time drinking coffee, talking, and having lots of fun.

I felt pride when Porter was elected President of the Betas, and when he graduated, and when he got an Alfred Sloan Fellowship.

I would *never* have told Porter this, of course. I would never have breathed a word to anyone that he and his friends were my role models. In fact, I'd never heard of a role model, but I surely did like hanging out with those guys when I had a chance.

It was Porter who suggested that, if I worked at it, I might get a scholarship to an Eastern college. I would never have thought of it myself.

It must be clear that the picture I am painting is of someone who was a great influence in my life. Of a person who *could* have kept me out of the longest Monopoly game in history, in Ben Stapleton's dining room, because big brothers can do that, you know, if they want to.

But Porter didn't. He let me in, he let me play. He was kind to me. He was a kind and gentle man. All his life. A gentleman. But you all know that. That's why you've come today. That's why Mary-Armour and I and our family have come, to join Polly and Jill and their families in celebrating Porter's life.

It was an important life. I've told you a few of the ways it was important to me, but it has been important to people far beyond the limits of family, or the limits of friendship. It has been important to people who never heard of Porter Nelson: People who suffer from arthritis, or people who get medical treatment at General Rose Hospital, or who take a swim at the "Y".

They don't know it, but they are feeling the kindness the gentleness, and the compassion of a great man, my brother Porter.

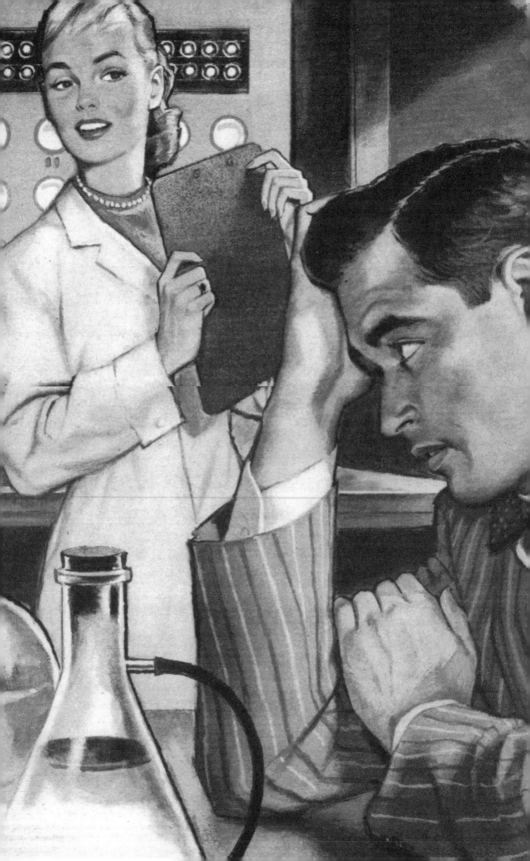

My Private War
With Herman

Philadelphia Inquirer Sunday Magazine
August 18, 1957

Besides knocking my alarm clock on the floor and hacking one cheek with my razor, I swallowed this piece of eggshell at breakfast. All the way from the fraternity house to the physics lab, I could feel it scraping around in my stomach. And then when I tried to open the front door of the lab, which was one of my student jobs, I remembered I'd left the darned key back on my bureau.

Dog-trotting back to the Newt house, I took a shortcut across the grass and stepped on this rake. It didn't stab through my foot or anything, but the handle flew up and crocked me right between the eyes. For the next five minutes I wandered around trying to recall a few interesting facts, such as the date, and what my name was, and after a while it came back to me: I was Peter Prentiss, and it was Monday, and I was already ten minutes late opening the lab.

When I got back to the lab, panting a little, old Professor Phipps was standing on the steps, waiting to be let in. He glared at me and said well, what's the excuse this time, and I said I got hit in the head by a rake handle. I can easily believe it, Prentiss, he said; how old were you when it happened? I said it just happened that morning, and he said oh and muttered something about why did they give him an English major for a lab assistant anyway? I tried to explain it was only temporary, and as he walked into the building, he said he prayed to God I was right.

I followed him in and went about my business and was just lowering the Venetian blinds on the sunny side of the downstairs lab when this girl walked in. I let go of the cord—I didn't mean to—and the blind came clattering down and socked me a glancing blow on the shoulder and sent up a big cloud of dust. I just stood there, looking.

This girl had on a starchy white lab coat with just a snatch of pearls and blue cashmere sweater peeking out at the throat, and short honey-colored hair curling all over her head. My brainwheels began to click, and it came to me she must be Elizabeth Whitman, the girl transfer from State. The professor had told me she was coming. I sucked in my breath and raced my engine a little and shined my left shoe on the back of my right pant leg, and then my right shoe on my left pant leg, and breezed on over to where she was standing. Good morning, Liz, I said, I'm Peter Prentiss, old Phipps' number-one boy, and welcome to Tioga U.

Oh, she said. Oh, thank you. But how did you know my name? I said well, old Phipps warned me you were coming, but he failed to mention you were so beautiful. She blushed a little and said oh again and then said which is my work space? I said right this way, Liz honey, and I showed her the work bench and cabinets I'd cleaned out for this new assistant professor, but which I'd just decided to give to her instead.

Anything I can do for you, I said, please call on me, and she said as a matter of fact, could I please bring in that big wooden box the expressman had left out in the hall? I said certainly and lugged in this big brass-bound box for her and started to set it down on the floor, and she said no, on the workbench please, so I started to dump it on the bench for her, and she said careful! Not too hard. You'll jar Herman.

I said you mean you've got an animal in this box? She laughed and said no, it was something far more delicate than an animal. She unscrewed some brass fittings and the lid of the box came up on hinges, and then the front came down on hinges, too, and all she had in the box was this old radio chassis chockfull of tubes and wires, with 20 or 30 dials on the front, and two long rows of colored lights.

This is Herman, I said? This is Herman, she said. Herman is nothing but a broken-down old radio, I said. And she said oh no, Herman was her pet thinking machine, and she'd built him herself. I said you mean he's an electronic whaddyacallit, and she said yes, he's an electronic digital computer, and I said yeah, that's what I meant.

She started to fiddle with Herman's insides, yanking tubes out and looking at them and putting them back, and I coughed a little to let her know I was still there and said if there was anything else she wanted, just let me know. She said thank you, Peter, and went on fiddling with Herman's table of contents, so after a few minutes I coughed again and said I was in the lab from eight to nine every morning, adjusting shades and getting old Phipps off to a flying start, and again in the afternoon from five to six, slowing him down. She said is that so?

I said yes, it was so, and by the way, did she know there was a big dance Friday night at the Student Union, and she said no, she didn't, and I said, well there is, and how about going to it with me?

She abandoned Herman then and stood up, and I got a whiff of this perfume of hers, and all I can say is that it took some of the sting out of her saying no. She was terribly sorry, she said, but she'd be working Friday night

Working, I said! And then I told her that nobody worked Friday nights except creeps and grinds, and she laughed and said she was a creep *and* a grind, and went back to fiddling with Herman.

Listen, I said, how about Saturday night then, we could take in a movie, and she said she'd be working Saturday night, too. So I tried Sunday, but darned if she wasn't going to work Sunday, so I said listen, did I do something to offend you, and she said heavens no, Peter, what made you think that?

Maybe I'm personally repulsive to you then, I said, and she said no, quite the contrary. So I said then how come you won't go out with me, say Friday to this dance, for example?

I just don't go out, she said. You don't go out, I said! You mean you don't go out ever?

No, she said, and I said, well for gosh sakes, why not? Well, it's a long story, she said, but it all boils down to the fact I want to be a physicist, not a housewife. Liz honey, I said, lots of girls have dated Peter Prentiss without becoming housewives.

Liz laughed at that and said I know, but if I went out with boys, sooner or later I might become romantically involved with one of them. She batted her big blue eyes at me. Maybe even you, she said.It's a possibility, I said. Yes, she said, and then the next thing, she'd wake up some morning a few years from now and find herself tending babies instead of electronic circuits, and I said what's so bad about that?

Nothing, she said, except that my father is a scientist. So what, I said and she said well, her father more than anything wanted her to be a scientist, too, and I said well what does your mother want you to be? She said her mother had died a year ago, which was another reason she didn't want to disappoint her father. I said I was sorry about her mother, and she said thanks, and then I said that as far as disappointing her father went, she'd be disappointing a lot more people if she stayed on this no-date kick.

She smiled, and I smiled, and then she went back to work on Herman, and I sort of stood there, looking at how smooth and tan her legs were—what showed of them—and noting how wonderful the right girl can look in one of those white coats. After a while I realized it was 9:15, and I was already late for my Chaucer class, so I said I've got to run, I'll see you later Liz honey, and she said good-by Peter, and thanks.

I came back to the lab a couple of hours early that afternoon.

Liz had old Herman out of his case and plugged in, and his colored lights were blinking on and off like a Christmas tree. I walked right over and said Liz, I've been thinking this date thing over, and the whole thing's ridiculous. Oh, she said? Yes, I said, it's the duty of all Tioga students to support university activities, of which this Friday dance is one. Oh, she said? Yes, I said, and I am going to see that you do your duty by dear old Tioga.

I'd love to, Peter, she said, smiling, but I can't.

I sucked in my breath and sat down on one of those tall lab stools. Liz, you make me feel bad, I said. Don't feel bad, she said. I can't help it, I said, I feel miserable. Here I want to take you out, I said, want to get acquainted and talk nuclear physics with you, but what do you say?

Are you interested in nuclear physics, she said?

Since this morning, I said. Only how can a lowly English major learn anything about the subject when the only really congenial physics major in the place refuses to go out with him? Refuses flatly, in fact. Leaves no room for hope. Not even a teensy-weensy little loophole.

Would you feel better if there were a teensy-weensy little loophole, she said? Yes, I said. What kind of loophole, she said?

I would like something, I said, that if I did it, you would go to the dance with me. You mean like swim the deepest ocean for me, she said? Yes, I said, or perhaps fetch something for you from the far ends of the earth, or perhaps slay some monster that hath thee in thrall. No monster hath me in thrall, she said, and I said oh yes one doth and she said what monster is it, and I said Herman.

Do you think you could slay Herman, she said, and I said I felt sure I could fracture every tube in his wiry little body. But she said no, I'd have to defeat Herman some other way if I wanted to take her out. And if I do defeat Herman, I said, will you promise to go out with me? She said nobody could defeat Herman, he was too smart, and I said but what if I do? Then I'll go to the dance with you, she said.

Hallelujah, I said! And how would you like me to go about

defeating Herman? You'll have to play Nim with him, she said. Nim, I said, what's Nim? It's Herman's favorite game, she said, and I said how about defeating Herman at my favorite game, and she said what was my favorite game, and I said come to think of it, Herman was the wrong sex. If it's a game of the mind, she said, Herman can play it, and I said it isn't a game of the mind.

Well then, she said, you'll have to play Nim, and I said OK, how do I play? We'll need a lot of counters, she said, poker chips or pennies or paper clips or something. So I said OK, excuse me a minute, and I loped on down the hall to old Phipps' office and knocked and he said come in, so I did. When he saw who it was, he frowned and said what do you want, with the emphasis on the *you*.

The new transfer student needs some paper clips, I said, and he said well can't you get paper clips without disturbing me, and I said no, I couldn't because he had all the paper clips in the building. Didn't you order some more like I told you, he said, and I said no, sir, I forgot, but I'll do it first thing tomorrow morning. Then I picked up his paper clip box and smiled and told him I'd have some more for him just as soon as I could, and I went back to Liz' bench and dumped the paper clips on her bench and said OK, let's Herman and me do battle.

Liz divided the clips into three piles, not counting them or anything. You and Herman take turns, she said. Each turn you can take one clip, or you can take a whole pile, or any amount in between. But only from one pile at a time. And then Herman gets to take as many as he wants, and then you again, and then Herman, and so on. The player who picks up the last paper clip wins. OK?

I said I doubt if that broken-down radio can pick up paper clips. Obviously, Liz said, Herman only does the thinking and tells me how many to pick up. OK, I said, let's get started, and Liz said go ahead, dragon-slayers first.

Well, I took five clips from the biggest pile—it seemed like a nice round number—and Liz counted the clips that were left in each pile and twirled four or five of Herman's dials. Herman clicked and flashed and even managed to buzz a little.

Liz looked at the lights and ran one hand through her curly blonde hair, and then she said Herman says to take two paper clips from the second pile. I didn't hear him say so, I said, and Liz said look at his lights, they tell you what he says. Well, they didn't tell me what he said, but then I hadn't built him. It was my turn again, so I took two clips from the first pile, and then Liz spun Herman's dials again, and Herman took the whole third pile, and before I knew it, there were just two piles left, with one paper clip in each, and it was my turn. I took one clip, and Herman took the other, and won.

Say, I said, let's try that again, but Liz said no, I've got to get to work. Liz, honey, I said, I demand a rematch! Liz laughed and said OK, Peter, tomorrow, and do you call everyone honey? Only you, I said, and Liz smiled and went back to work.

I wasn't too upset over my defeat, because I figured Herman had won on a fluke, so the next morning when I opened the lab— right on time, too—I was determined to play more carefully. Liz came in about ten minutes after eight, looking like a flower that had just opened, and I walked over and said Liz honey, I'm ready to flatten Herman. Liz laughed and said give him time to warm up, so we plugged Herman in and let him warm up while we made a pot of coffee over her Bunsen burner. And then Herman and I played Nim, and even though I played it plenty cagey, Herman clobbered me in three turns.

Liz unplugged Herman, and his glowing red lights went off. She finished her coffee, and I watched as she slipped her lab coat over that gorgeous figure. Finally I said, tell me this, Liz honey, is it impossible to beat Herman? Not impossible, Peter, she said, merely improbable. Perhaps, I said, perhaps there is a source of information on this game of Nim? There is, she said. And where would one find it, I said? Liz threw her arms back and stretched and said do you think I'm going to help you upset my plan to become Liz Whitman, Girl Scientist?

That night I cornered Louie Pearson, who is a mathematician and a brother Newt, and I said Louie, you're a mathematician and a brother Newt, and I need some help. I'm broke already, Louie said. Louie, I said, I don't need money, I need knowledge about a game called Nim. I've heard of it, Louie said. Louie, I said, I am a very poor Nim player, and I wish to improve my game.

Well, Louie said, it just takes a little simple algebra, and I said fine, Louie, show me this simple algebra, please. Well, Louie said, all you've got to do to win is to reduce the three piles to "2n, 2n plus 1, and 1." Come again, I said?

Well, Louie is a good brother Newt, and after working with him for a couple of hours, I began to get the big picture.

I felt pretty jaunty when I unlocked the physics building the next morning. I made some coffee at Liz's workbench and looked at Herman's lights and dials, thinking how I was going to lick the socks off him in a few minutes. Finally, about ten after eight, Liz came in wearing a clinging blue wool dress that demonstrated clearly she was cut out for motherhood and not science.

Well, after the coffee and small talk we got the paper clips out and went to work. I could barely conceal my smile as I counted the three piles and did some figuring on a piece of yellow paper to find out how to reduce them to 2n, 2n plus 1, and 1, like Louie said I should. Finally I made a move, and Herman made a move, and I made another, and in something under a minute and a half, Herman—that is, Liz—picked up the last paper clip.

Liz honey, I said, crumpling my paper, how can a nice girl like you be so cruel? It wasn't me who beat you, Liz said, it was Herman. But you built Herman, I said.

Peter, Liz said, smiling sort of sadly, please, Peter, you make it awfully hard for me. I make it hard for you, I said? Yes, she said, it isn't easy to dedicate oneself to Science, and try to fight down one's instincts, and...

The purpose of instincts, I said, is definitely not to fight them down. Look at me—am I fighting down my instincts?

That night I told Louie he was a bum. Didn't you do what I said, Louie asked me? I tried to, I said, but Herman never left me in a position to do it. Herman, Louie said, is he the guy you play against? Herman is a machine, I said. You mean a computer, Louie said? That's right, I said. Well, in that case, Louie said, you better learn something quick about binary numbers. That's what computers think in. Explain, I said.

Well, Louie didn't understand binary numbers any too well himself, but he knew a guy named Smitty over at the Pea-Pod house who did. So I walked across the campus in the moonlight, thinking of Liz, and I found Smitty in the kitchen of the Pea-Pod house, making himself a sandwich, and I told him my problem.

Well, Smitty said, chewing up a big mouthful, the binary number system is just like our decimal system, only instead of using zero, one, two, three and so on up through nine, you just use zero and one. Get it? No, I said. Well, he said, it's like this: Zero in the decimal system is the same as zero in the binary system. Get that? I got it, I said. All right, he said, and one in the decimal system is the same as one in the binary system. Get that? I got it, I said. OK, he said, then two in the decimal system obviously becomes one-zero in the binary system, doesn't it. Smitty, I said, standing up hopelessly, I'll see you around.

I was lying in bed when I got my big idea. It was like discovering radar or inventing the wheel or something, and I knew sure it was going to do the trick. I lay back and relaxed and shut my eyes and dreamed up a big, wide-screen picture of me and Liz, just the way we would be dancing that coming Friday to the music of Skinny Cigarillo and his Matchless Five.

I got to the lab nearly an hour early the next morning, and the first thing I did was to let all the blinds down so no one could see in. Then I walked over to Liz' workbench. Old Herman was sitting there smug and sleepy with his lights out, resting up so he could annihilate me later in the morning.

But not this morning! No, sir! Old Herman hadn't counted on me leaning around behind his back and reaching into his tangled insides and plucking out a tube! I didn't take a big tube, or even a very impressive looking one, but just one that was centrally located and wouldn't be missed unless you craned your neck to see. I stuck the tube in my pocket, and then I went out the front door of the physics building and locked it, and wandered around humming a little rock-and-roll number until it was eight o'clock, my regular time to open up.

At 8:10 I was out in the front hall, waiting for Liz to show her pretty face. At 8:20 I was still waiting. At 8:30 I went into old Phipps' office and checked my watch against the gold clock on his desk. Finally, about five of nine, I had to go to class. I felt awful. Half of me was worried that Liz was sick or hurt or something, and the other, grosser part of me was worried she would arrive just after I'd left, discover Herman wasn't working, and have all day to figure out what I'd done to him.

I had a miserable day. Between the Nineteenth Century Novel and waiting table at the Beta Squaw sorority, and Philosophy 122, and a million other things, I didn't get back to the lab till almost closing time. It was just beginning to get dark outside, and I was afraid Liz would be gone. Everyone else was.

When I walked into the big, empty, downstairs lab, though, there she was, looking scrumptious in a yellow skirt and a nice, snug, yellow sweater. When she saw me, she looked up and smiled, and somehow it wasn't such a miserable day after all.

Liz honey, I said, I missed you this morning. I drew in a big, deep breath—she smelled like violets with a lot of nice, fresh dew on them. I missed you, too, she said, and I felt warm all over. I felt pretty sure she hadn't found out about Herman, or she wouldn't have said that and smiled the way she did.

Liz honey, where were you this morning, I asked, and she told me she had a class Thursday mornings, and then she asked me what I'd been doing, and.. finally we plugged Herman in.

Liz laid out the paper clips, and I played first and took three clips from the second pile. Liz fiddled with Herman's dials for a couple of seconds and Herman blinked his lights and took two clips from the same pile. Then I played, and then Herman played, and then I played once more. Liz spun old Herman's dials around and the lights blinked, and when they glowed steady again, Liz looked at them, and at the paper clips, and frowned. Then she spun the dials again, and the lights blinked some more, and Liz looked at them, and then at the paper clips, and frowned again, and then she cocked her head on one side and looked at me. Then she unplugged Herman and turned the plug over and plugged him back in again and spun the dials another time and waited till the lights quit blinking and were steady again.

Something the matter? I said.

Liz looked at the lights and shook her curly head and figured for a minute on a piece of paper, and then she looked up at me with those big blue eyes of hers and said, I just don't understand.

Understand what, I said.

Liz bit her lip and twirled Herman's dials around once more, adjusting them ever so carefully this time, and then she read the lights and said I don't know how you did it, Peter, but you've won. In one more play, you've got Herman licked.

This was the moment I'd been awaiting so eagerly, my moment of victory! She had to go to the dance with me now!

But...it was funny. I didn't feel half as good about it as I should have. I mean, just standing there, looking into those puzzled, wide, blue eyes, it began to seem kind of mean and unfair. Here I was, tricking a lovely, dedicated, innocent young girl into doing something her heart was dead set against. I mean, you can do that to some people, but not to someone...well, someone you care for.

Maybe Herman wasn't warmed up enough, I said. Maybe we

ought to try him later on. I sort of figured I could slip the tube back in when Liz wasn't looking, and then Herman could go ahead and give me the usual pasting.

No, he was warmed up, Liz said. Well, maybe he's got a short in his liver or something, I said. We all makes mistakes. Tell you what, we'll give him another try in the morning.

No, Liz said, very serious, no, I'm a woman of my word, Peter. I will go to the dance with you.

The way she said it, it did something to me. Something deep down inside. I knew I had to tell her.

Liz, I said, you don't have to go to that dance with me. I do, too, she said. Herman lost, didn't he? Yes, I said, but you don't understand. Don't understand what, she said? Liz, I said, I've got a confession to make. I...I cheated.

Liz's wide blue eyes got even wider. You cheated, she said? I felt like a robber with my hand caught in the till. I reached into my trouser pocket and pulled out this insignificant little tube and laid it on the counter beside Liz' coffee pot.

I took it out of Herman this morning, I said.

You didn't, Liz said!

I could have crawled under the linoleum, I felt that small.

You mean to say, Liz said, you were going to risk upsetting my whole career just so I'd go to a dance with you?

I'm...I'm afraid so, I said, hanging my head. Then I looked up. But Liz honey, I said, Liz when I looked into your beautiful, big, blue eyes, I just couldn't go through with it, Liz, honey!

But Peter, why not? Liz said.

Well, I said, if you...well, if you like a person enough...if you think enough of them... Yes, she said?

Well, I said, let me put it this way: If you were as crazy about me as I am about you, you wouldn't be able to do anything as despicable as I have done, and... Liz said, I wouldn't?

No, I said, and furthermore...

But the way she was smiling at me—a really strange smile—I quit talking. And then she reached her hand into the side pocket of her yellow skirt and held it there for a second, and then pulled it out in a sort of fist and held it up under my nose, and then she opened it.

My jaw dropped halfway to the floor. Liz, I said! Where'd *that* tube come from?

She just rolled her big blue eyes in the direction of Herman's glowing red lights, and then rolled them back in my direction, which made me sort of light up, myself. I mean, all of a sudden I didn't feel so mean and unfair after all, and besides, I'd just thought of a number of things I'd been meaning to tell Liz—about her nose, for example, which was the straightest, cutest little nose you ever saw, and her lips...

Well, anyhow, I was supposed to lock the lab up at six, but what with one thing and another, I guess I didn't get around to it till nearly midnight. I knew old Professor Phipps wouldn't mind, though. After all, we weren't using any electricity.

Meyer Friedman, M.D.
1910-2001

My Friend Mike Friedman

Palace of the Legion of Honor,
San Francisco, May 18, 2001

Seventeen years ago, when I had only known Mike Friedman for 25 years, he gave me a book. Mike gave me many books over the years, but this one was hot off the press. It was a sequel to his first Type A book, and it was called, *"Treating Type A Behavior and Your Heart."*

Inside the front cover he'd written a note. I have it here. It says *"To Jim,"* which is followed by a couple of personal remarks, and then it says:

> *"Perhaps you might be interested to know that I've asked that you speak at my forthcoming Memorial Service, after I have been called to see the "Old Man." This isn't morbid—I'm smiling as I write this. And Jim, make the speech short, remember some of my best friends are Type A"*

> *"Your Friend, Mike. September 14, 1984"*

Mary-Armour and I met Mike in October, 1959, at a meeting of the American Association of Advertising Agencies, at the Santa Barbara Biltmore. Mike and I both were speakers.

My speech took a look into a future so distant it seemed as though it might never come. It was titled, *"1992."*

Mike's talk was a real eye-opener. It was titled, *"How to Have a Heart Attack."*

I think we've all heard that speech, under a variety of titles. It became a perpetual work in progress for Mike, never the same twice, and always bringing the latest news from the world of time urgency, free-floating hostility, and behavior modification.

Tonight, however, I'm laying aside all of Mike's famous speeches, his discoveries, his awards, his professional articles, his books for medical and lay audiences, all his laurels. I want to talk about the Mike Friedman I remember best, the one I always looked forward to seeing, who was not a scientist, not a doctor, but simply a friend.

When I try to catalog what I remember about Mike, I come up with an assortment of memories, some very trivial.

I remember, for example, a breakfast Mary-Armour and I had with Mike and Macia in Hawaii. It was another conference, and Mike was a speaker. He ordered a papaya—nothing memorable in that—but then he called for a pepper-grinder. He proceeded to cover the papaya with coarsely ground pepper, until it was quite black. Then he ate it, enjoying every bite.

Obviously, this called for a clinical trial to see if Mike's enjoyment could be replicated. So, I ordered a papaya. Mike passed me the pepper-grinder. And I discovered, for the first but not the last time, how brilliant Mike really was. Because, papaya, smothered in ground black pepper, is astonishingly good.

When you try it, think of Mike.

A lot of my memories of Mike seem to be associated with food, wine, and restaurants. We had a lot of our lunches at the Fior d'Italia, and I will never forget one lunch—it must have been in the 60's—when it was my turn to play host.

As we looked at the menu, Mike said, "Jim, have you ever sent a bottle of wine back?"

I thought a minute, and said, "Never."

Mike said, "Today, let's send it back."

In due course I ordered a bottle of—and I remember this perfectly—Louis Martini Zinfandel.

Our waiter returned with a bottle and started his routine. He showed me the label. I nodded. He cut the foil, pulled the cork, and handed it to me. He poured a splash of red wine into my glass, and stood erect, polite but faintly absent. It was something he'd done a thousand times.

I swirled the wine, smelled it, tasted it, and frowned.

"I'm not sure about this wine," I said. "It seems, mmm, *off* somehow. Why don't you let the doctor taste it."

The waiter came fully awake at last. He said, "Pour some for him?"

I nodded, and Mike got a splash of Zinfandel.

He swirled it, smelled it, tasted it. And then *he* frowned.

He said, "There's something wrong here."

The waiter was dumbfounded.

I said, "I think you'd better get us another bottle."

Amazingly, the next bottle turned out to be just fine. And later, mid-lunch, the *maitre'd* came to our booth and said, "I tasted that wine in the kitchen, and I agree—it's definitely off."

I think back to another lunch with Mike at the Fior, after the market had taken some kind of nosedive. Halfway through lunch a two-man TV news crew walked in. With a little guidance from the *maitre'd,* they approached our booth. The cameraman focused on Mike, and the reporter said, "Dr. Friedman?"

Mike said, "Yes, what can I do for you?"

The reporter asked him whether, in light of the sagging market, the economy was still sound. He wanted Dr. Friedman's opinion on the long-term outlook. Should investors be scared?

Mike looked thoughtful, then rambled on to the effect that the economy certainly seemed sound. He didn't think people needed to worry. He said the long-term outlook was definitely positive.

The reporter thanked him. He and his cameraman left, and Mike laughed.

He said, "They think I'm *Milton* Friedman."

Over time, we both made some changes in our lunch habits.

We moved from the bottle of wine to a double decaf espresso for Mike, and a Pellegrino water for me. And Mike moved from the eggplant parmagiana to the calamari saute´.

"But," he would say, with a finger held in the air, "only the tentacles."

At the Fior, thanks to my long association with Mike, I am known as "Doctor Nelson."

"How are you, Doctor Nelson?"

"What will you have today, Doctor Nelson?"

Nobody ever asks me what kind of doctor I am, and I live in perpetual fear I may be asked to deliver a baby.

I learned a lot from Mike. He never set out to teach me anything. I just learned by hanging around. It was what we would now call an interactive course—the communication flowed both ways between student and teacher. And, since the course was 42 years long, we had the chance to cover a lot of subjects.

It was fun to be with Mike. He ranged so widely, he enjoyed so many things, he gave so much of himself.

When I think of Mike's being called to see the "Old Man," I think of a quotation from the first book he ever gave me. That book is titled, *"The Human Situation."* The author is Macneile Dixon, late Professor of English Literature from the University of Glasgow.

The quotation is from the first chapter, in which Dixon confesses his personal preferences, so the reader will be aware of his biases. He says,

"Of the more highly praised virtues—save courage and magnanimity—I am deficient in appreciation, and the heaven of my choice would, I fear, contain but few saints or examples of moral perfection. Indeed, I am not sure it would contain any. It would be mainly peopled by agreeable sinners, not too unlike myself for companionship."

I hope Mike runs into Macneile Dixon. They would get along famously. I hope he also meets his idol Marcel Proust, and Jesse James. Mike did a lot of research on Jesse thinking he might write a book about him. He did a lot of it on site, in Missouri, and I know he still has a lot of questions for Jesse.

I'll close with two observations about Mike.

The first is that, while Mike had many talents in many areas of the world's activities, he had one talent that led all the others. That was his talent for friendship.

Look at all of us here. We're living proof. We knew a lot about Mike, but he knew more about us. He asked about us, about our wives, husbands, families, jobs, our interests. He wanted to know about us, and he remembered who and what we were, and when it was appropriate, he gave us help.

A talent for friendship. It's a great gift. And we are the beneficiaries of Mike's gift.

My second observation concerns one of the very early things I remember Mike talking about: Memory. Mike felt that everyone, every day, Type A and Type B alike, should find something in that day worthy of remembering. Then, a day later, a year later, a lifetime later, you could take those memories out and enjoy them.

I feel grateful that I, and Mary-Armour, and our children, all have a supply of different Mike Friedman memories to take out and enjoy.

One of my enjoyable memories dates back to 1976, when Mike gave me a slender volume by a man named Williston Fish. I had expressed interest in it, and without telling me, Mike bought it for me at a book auction.

The book is titled, *"A Last Will,"* and purports to be a father writing his last will and testament.

It's written in proper legal language, but it's still very poetic. He speaks of *"leaving to children exclusively...all and every the dandelions of the fields and the daisies thereof, with the right to play among them freely, according to the custom of children."*

A couple of weeks ago, I reread Williston Fish's *"A Last Will."* As I read, it occurred to me that the last paragraph of the will might very well have been written by Mike, for the rest of us.

In the paragraphs preceding, the writer has left special gifts to children, to youths, and to lovers, and he concludes his will thus:

> *"Item: And to those who are no longer children, or youths, or lovers, I leave Memory, and I leave to them the volumes of the poems of Burns and Shakespeare, and of other poets, if there are others, to the end that they may live the old days over again freely and fully, without tithe or diminution; and to those who are no longer children, or youths, or lovers, I leave, too, the knowledge of what a rare, rare world it is."*

Mike could have said that. He probably did.
Thank you.

Mike Friedman (r.) and long-time luncheon companion at a reception to celebrate establishment of the Meyer Friedman Chair of Medical Research at the University of California Medical School, San Francisco.

APRIL 14th IN

FRY'S LANDING

Good Housekeeping, August 1957

When Patrolman George Skelton, barefoot, stepped on an up-turned thumbtack in his bedroom at 3:35 a.m. on the morning of April 14th, he felt certain that "one of those days" was coming up. He could even predict the giant calamity with which the day would grind to its climax: The Fry's Landing City Council, which was due to fill the vacant job of police chief that afternoon, would not fill it with George Skelton.

In a few hours people all over Fry's Landing would be getting up, feeling the same way Skelton did. Some would have headaches; some, hangovers; some, insoluble problems. Some, as they awoke, would be certain they hadn't slept a wink all night. All would be positive of one thing: A difficult day lay ahead.

Having disposed of the thumbtack, Skelton hobbled to the bathroom to shave. Afterward he put on a fresh blue shirt and muttered a little when he noted that his wife hadn't mended a tear just below the pocket. He felt it was another omen.

Actually, it wasn't much of a tear, but Skelton thought it didn't look right on an officer of the law, so he pinned his badge low to cover it. In the mirror, the star looked odd that low on the shirt, but Skelton decided it would look even worse with the torn place showing. While he drank his first cup of coffee, he checked his Smith & Wesson .38 Police Special. It was loaded.

At exactly 4:00 a.m., as Skelton was starting his patrol of Fry's Landing in the new police car, nineteen-year-old Donna Prentiss, who lived on the other, better, side of town, stirred in her sleep. Her tangled brown hair tumbled about her face as she burrowed deeper in her pillow, dreaming of Fulton Burrows, twenty-one, who was to take her boating at ten that morning. Fulton—in the dream—was pulling Donna toward him in a savage embrace, kissing her roughly on her neck, cheek, lips, forehead, and both ears.

Two and three-quarter hours later Donna would awaken with a vague sense of uneasiness. Had she made a mistake, she would wonder, in practically forcing shy, handsome Fulton Burrows into today's boating engagement?

At 4:32 a.m., in a two-story Georgian house at 4 Catalpa Road, a few blocks from Donna Prentiss's house, Mrs. Frederick Burrows urgently tugged at her husband's pajama top until he woke up.

"Fred, I smell smoke," she said.

Fred Burrows yawned wearily and sat up in bed.

"You're always smelling smoke," he said.

"It smells strong, Fred," she insisted. "Go look, please."

Fred Burrows slowly got up and put on his slippers and his bathrobe. "How come you never smell smoke except when I'm sound asleep?" he asked.

Then he went downstairs to look in every room, ending up in the basement; but he was unable to find smoke or fire. On his way back to bed, he noticed a crack of light showing under his son's door. He wondered momentarily what Fulton could be doing up at this hour. He decided not to ask, though. Sometimes of late he didn't really understand his son.

Behind the closed bedroom door, Fulton, who in about five hours was to embark with Donna Prentiss on a pleasure cruise down the Wenatchee River, was sitting on the edge of his bed, alternately reading from two books. One volume was entitled *Oars and Oarsmen*, the other, *Water Safety*. Fulton had checked them out of the Fry's Landing Free Public Library the evening before, shortly after a chance meeting and extended conversation with the lovely Donna Prentiss in Smallberg's Drugstore. The conversation had somehow resulted in his asking her to go—Fulton shuddered—boating! Only twice in his life had he been in a boat of any kind, and neither time at the oars; his family had recently moved to Fry's Landing from a landlocked wheat farm in Kansas.

Between six and seven, a good many people in Fry's Landing woke up with symptoms, physical and mental, that gave them reason to consider the coming day. In an apartment building at 141 Swanscott Way, for example, Ezra Donaldson, fifty-five, unmarried, a teller in the Fry's Landing First National Bank, opened his sad eyes, only to close them instantly, thinking, as he frequently did, of the $3,500 he had embezzled from the bank during the past three months.

Across town, near the junction of Lincoln Street and Wintoon Alley, in the ancient building that housed the Fry's Landing Volunteer Fire Company Number One, Frisbie Collins, the one paid member of the unit, lapsed from a drugged sleep into a woozy semi-consciousness, regretting his libations of the night before.

Seven blocks away, at 6 Catalpa Road, next door to the Burrows house, Emma Skidmore, whose husband Al was away on business in Boise, Idaho, awoke feeling lonely and blue. It was bad enough that Albert Skidmore had to travel, Emma thought, but this time he had gone off angry. And she had stayed behind angry. Married four years, they were a devoted couple. Usually when Al took off for Boise or Portland, Emma went with him. While he conducted his business, she walked around looking in windows and sometimes doing a bit of shopping.

It had started with the hat. One day while she had been ambling through a department store in Portland, Emma had fallen in love with a blue hat trimmed with artificial daisies. To any objective eye, the hat looked top-heavy on Emma, who was small and fragile and had a slender neck, but Emma's eye was not objective. Although the hat had been ridiculously expensive ($14.95) and much too big to be concealed from Al (it came in a large box), she had bought it. She'd stowed it among the sample cases in the back of the car so that it hadn't been detected until Al was unloading the car back in Fry's Landing.

"What's this?" he'd asked as he had hauled it out.

"Oh," said Emma. "Wait'll you see it."

"So, what is it?" Al had pursued.

"You wait," Emma had teased.

The upshot of it was that when she'd come tripping down the stairs that night in the big boater, Al had burst into howls of laughter.

Emma had been shattered.

"You don't *like* it?" she cried.

"Hello, Hat, where's Emma?" Al had asked before going off into more gales.

"I'll have you know it cost fourteen dollars and ninety-five cents!" Emma had said, enraged. "It's the latest style!"

"You mean you paid nearly fifteen dollars for that thing?" Al had said. "As hard as I have to work?"

Emma had now been really piqued. "You think nothing of paying a hundred dollars for a rifle,'" she'd cried, "to shoot at defenseless animals!" Then she'd begun to cry.

She had touched him in a sensitive area. Emma was always complaining of Al's hunting trips, from which she was excluded, naturally, and what few disagreements they'd ever had had derived from these trips. Also, it always made Al nervous when Emma cried. So he'd shouted at her and made her cry harder.

Then she had begun to pout, and they'd found themselves unable to speak to each other for a couple of days. This had been a great privation for affectionate Emma, who hadn't known what to do with herself. Al had been stubborn and gone off to Boise without kissing her good-by. He'd put his newest deer rifle in the front seat on the chance that he might pick off some game en route. The sight of the rifle on the seat instead of herself made Emma wild. By the time April 14th rolled around, she felt as if it might be the end of the world. Deciding that she could not stay in the empty house another minute, she planned to go to town as soon as the stores opened. Since Al wasn't there to twit her, she would get whatever use she could from the blue hat with the daisies by wearing it to town.

At exactly 7:00 a.m., Patrolman Skelton, who had now been on duty three hours, parked the shiny black-and-white patrol car in front of Gaspar's Grill and went in for another cup of coffee. Although he still harbored a feeling of impending disaster, he addressed Harry Elmo, who had leased Gaspar's Grill from the First National Bank next door, with his usual greeting.

"Hello, Gaspar," George Skelton teased.

"Aw, lay off, George," Elmo replied. "I don't feel so hot this morning."

"Yeah? Me, too. But say, Harry, when are you going to get a new sign painted on that window? Make it Elmo's Grill, or Harry's Hash House, or something."

"When I get the money, that's when!" Elmo replied testily.

Having drawn a cup of steaming black coffee from the glistening urn, he set it in front of Skelton. "You know what that skinflint Alvin wants for painting a new sign? Sixty dollars!"

From 7:04 till 7:17, Donna Prentiss sat in front of her dressing table, brushing her hair. She brushed it a hundred times, hoping that the activity would quiet the vague uneasiness she felt from having engineered Fulton into the boating date. Her shining brown hair, attractively framing her young face, glistened and curled as it sprang back from the brush, but the sight did not allay her feeling of uneasiness.

In the Burrows household, on the other hand, Fulton's mother, who had smelled smoke during the night and who had awakened with a headache, which made her cross, suddenly felt a slight lessening of tension. She had just broken two eggs into a frying pan, one for her husband, the other for Fulton. Both had double yolks!

This incident buoyed her up considerably. She decided then to report it to the *Daily Sentinel* later in the morning and to go shopping afterward.

But there was no easing of tension for her son Fulton. While he was eating one of the double-yolked eggs, Fulton painfully tried to visualize an illustration in *Water Safety*. Did the rower face the front of the boat (bow), Fulton wondered, or the rear (stern)?

Next door, at the Skidmore house, Emma was morosely eating an ordinary soft-boiled, single-yolked egg that was too soft. To add to her gloom, she had broken a coffee cup before breakfast and now had the hiccups.

Breakfast in bank-teller Ezra Donaldson's bachelor apartment on Swanscott Way consisted of a glass of orange juice and two raw eggs, mixed in an electric blender. Between gulps, Ezra gnawed at a stubby yellow pencil, not from hunger, but from desperation. He was trying hard to shut out the sound of the organ music that drifted in from the nearby Fourth Street Church while he doped out the third race at Bay Meadows from the inadequate information on the *Daily Sentinel's* sports page.

At the same moment, another Fry's Landing citizen, Colton Everhard, was also hearing the organ music in the bathroom of his large three-story, colonial house on Linden Place. Apparently fate had overlooked Everhard, for he was whistling along with the organ and experiencing absolutely no uneasiness.

Everhard, incidentally, might well have attended the Fourth Street Church that morning to ask remission of his sins, for he was a sinner of some magnitude. In fact, at that very moment, he was reviewing his plan to abandon his wife and four children, and to leave town that afternoon—and the country the following day; the passports were all arranged—with a titian-haired , twenty-four-year-old stenographer, whose name is of no importance.

Everhard had already packed his securities in a Gladstone bag, along with pajamas and a silk dressing gown. The bag was now reposing, slightly squashed, in the large safe at his office. Everhard was preparing to abandon not only his family, but also the lucrative personal-finance company he had single-handedly established. The latter decision was not so difficult as it might seem, for Everhard was well aware that state and federal investigators were racing each other to be first with sufficient evidence to indict him on a number of charges; he was incontestably guilty.

At 10:19, while Fulton Burrows was nervously helping Donna Prentiss into a rowboat, someone, unidentified, turned in an alarm to Volunteer Fire Company Number One. At the time Frisbie Collins, whose condition had been ameliorated by a judicious eye opener (hair-of-the-dog), was reclining in his hammock on the second floor of the rickety firehouse. When he received the alarm, he slowly and carefully rose, grimaced, and shook his head. He then slid recklessly down the pole to the first floor, touched off the town's fire horn, and started to drive the number-one pumper toward Eighth and Oakdale. It was a false alarm.

Colton Everhard, meanwhile, was phoning the red-haired stenographer from his empty office.

"It's all set, honey," he said. "Pick you up at three."

At 11:07, in the lobby of the bank, teller Ezra Donaldson shakily dialed his bookie on the pay phone.

"Third at Bay Meadows," he breathed into the phone. "Two hundred on Nineveh. To win."

Ezra Donaldson's hands were still shaking as he reentered his cage. What a day! He was sure he had an ulcer. Nineveh was a long shot—twenty to one. But he had to have a long shot if he was going to replace that $3,500! If Nineveh didn't come in... Ezra sighed and adjusted his flowered arm bands.

Twenty-four minutes later, at 11:31, things began to happen thick and fast. On the Wenatchee River, the rowboat bearing the young couple overturned. Donna Prentiss screamed for help and waited hopefully for Fulton to rescue her. No one was in sight on either bank.

At 11:32, while Donna was flailing the water, a black four-door sedan pulled to a halt in front of the Fry's Landing First National Bank. A large man, with his right hand in his coat pocket, got out, nervously looked both ways, and entered the bank. A second man, the driver, stayed at the wheel and kept the motor running.

At 11:33, it became apparent to Donna Prentiss that Fulton Burrows was sinking out of sight for the second time. She, therefore, stopped treading water and dived after him. Although he seized her with maniacal frenzy, she was able to bring him to the surface. By biting his shoulder, she made him release her; then she swam around behind him, hooked her arm under his chin, and dragged him to shore.

Also at 11:33, on the first floor of the five-and-ten, two doors down the block from the bank, Mrs. Albert Skidmore and Fulton's mother, Mrs. Burrows, discovered they were wearing identical hats of blue straw dotted here and there with daisies. The discovery gave the two neighbors the giggles.

"Well, well," said Emma Skidmore. "I certainly do admire your taste, Marian!"

"Yours, too!"

"I got mine in Portland," said Emma Skidmore.

"I got mine in Groversville," said Marian Burrows.

For a moment the two ladies stared at each other. Then Emma Skidmore said, "Well, I suppose I should be upset, but I'm not in the least. Let's go next door to Gaspar's for a soda."

As the two ladies walked arm in arm from the five-and-ten to Gaspar's, Patrolman George Skelton noticed that the black car waiting in front of the bank with its motor running had a Vermont license plate. Skelton's eyes narrowed as this information was transferred from the optic nerve to the brain. That made 12 different out-of-state cars he'd seen since he came on duty at 4:00 a.m. (Vermont, Texas, Illinois, Indiana, Ohio, California, Kentucky, Wisconsin, Michigan, Florida, New York, and a real collector's item, Hawaii)! In addition, Skelton had seen two very good poker hands on license plates from his own state—one, a full house (2H2323, deuces over treys); the other, a straight (1133425).

At a few seconds after 11:34, inside the bank, the large man, who had been hovering near the stand-up desk, as though making out a deposit slip, moved to Ezra Donaldson's window and thrust a snub-nosed .45-caliber Colt revolver into Donaldson's face.

"Don't sound the alarm, Bub," the big man said, "unless you want a hole in your head. Just put all your bills in this bag and hand it to me. Fast!"

Ezra Donaldson's hands shook even more violently than they had when he'd phoned his bookie. But, he did as he'd been told: He loaded greenbacks into the cloth moneybag and opened his wicket to push it out to the gunman. At that exact instant, Colton Everhard entered the front door of the bank to close out the account he held jointly with the long-suffering wife whom he had determined to leave.

Colton Everhard was nothing if not observant. "Help! Police!" he shouted and turned to flee out the street door.

The first bullet dropped him, gasping, in his tracks. The gunman seized the moneybag and ran for the door, leaping over Everhard's writhing body.

"Stop him! Thief!" Ezra Donaldson shouted.

Patrolman Skelton was trying to work a poker hand out of the black sedan's license when he heard the shot. Drawing his gun immediately, he started toward the bank. Pedestrians stopped, then scattered as the robber emerged from the bank, gun in hand. Skelton fired and missed. The gunman jumped into the black sedan; the motor roared; the car leapt away from the curb. Skelton fired at a back tire and shattered the sedan's rear window. A gun barked from the car; the bullet crashed through Gaspar's front window and lodged in the oak back bar, behind the milk-shake machine. Fortunately, it missed the big mirror.

In the street, the sedan gathered speed. Skelton fired twice at the gas tank, but missed the car altogether.

The sedan was careening around the corner of Benton and Main, about to go out of sight, when Skelton fired his fifth and sixth shots. Albert Skidmore, who had been giving himself a bad time ever since he'd left for Boise without kissing Emma good-by, had returned two days early and was now driving anxiously down Benton Avenue. When Skelton's bullets suddenly began to whiz past Al's ears, he, in confusion, turned his car into the path of the oncoming automobile. Skelton's sixth bullet missed the gunman's car, but it sank into Al Skidmore's front tire, preventing his car from operating and thus creating a roadblock. The gunman's car lurched, skidded sideways, jumped the curb, decapitated a fire hydrant, and overturned. The first geyser of hydrant water spurted a spectacular 35 feet into the air. In the resulting moisture and commotion, the two gunmen crawled out a window of the wrecked car, one man still clutching the money sack, and disappeared down Wintoon Alley.

Reloading on the way, Patrolman Skelton ran after them through the cascading water.

"Mobilize the auxiliary!" he shouted hoarsely to anyone who cared to listen.

In Gaspar's Grill, Harry Elmo threw his white chef's cap into the air.

"Hot dog!" he said. "Now the insurance company's got to pay for a new window. Right? Well, they can pay for a new sign, too!"

At 11:48, on the west bank of the Wenatchee River, Fulton Burrows, stretched out on his back and, apparently recovered though somewhat damp, asked Donna Prentiss if she wanted to go back to town for lunch. Donna, who was holding Fulton's head in her lap, looked into his face and smiled warmly.

"No," she said. "Do you?"

Returning the smile, Fulton dreamily said, no, he wasn't hungry.

The police volunteer auxiliary, including member Ezra Donaldson, mobilized swiftly just as soon as Georgianna Philpott, the town clerk, found the list of their telephone numbers, which had been mislaid. With deer rifles, shotguns, and assorted pistols, they converged on the four-block-square, semi-commercial area where Patrolman Skelton declared the two gunmen were hiding. Of the entire group, no one had his heart in his work less than bank-teller Donaldson, who now reasoned that if the money was not recovered, he might somehow claim that the embezzled $3,500 had been stolen at gunpoint.

At 1:17, the sun was shedding maximum warmth on the banks of the Wenatchee, where Donna and Fulton sat entwined—quite innocently—in each other's arms.

"Why don't you ask me to go steady, darling?" Donna said.

Fulton Burrows laughed nervously. "Well...all right," he said. "I will. Will you...will you go steady?"

Donna closed her dark, shining eyes and buried her face in the curve of Fulton's chin.

"Yes," she sighed.

At 1:56, fireman Frisbie Collins, who had been taking a little something for his stomach's sake, heard noises downstairs in the firehouse. He ignored them and settled comfortably back into his hammock.

At the corner of Wintoon Alley and Lincoln Street, Patrolman Skelton turned to teller Donaldson and the other three volunteers in his group, then nodded significantly toward the firehouse.

"They're in there," he said quietly. "Get the tear gas."

Colton Everhard continued to sink rapidly and, at 2:17 p.m., died in the County Hospital, without ever regaining consciousness. Present at his bedside was his wife, who became the sole beneficiary of, among other things, a $100,000 life-insurance policy that Everhard had not yet transferred to the stenographer. Also present to condole with Mrs. Everhard was Everhard's sister, who had been summoned hurriedly from Groversville, along with Doctor Blaisdell (young Doctor Blaisdell, not his father) and a nurse.

At 2:21, while Donna Prentiss and Fulton Burrows were slowly strolling hand in hand down shrub-lined Lincoln Street, Patrolman Skelton, from behind a bush on the firehouse side of Lincoln, hurled the first tear-gas bomb. The bomb described a perfect parabola, struck the right front fender of the bright-red number-one pumper, and fell to the firehouse floor.

"Nice shot, George," whispered teller Donaldson.

Three seconds later, the tear-gas bomb described another perfect parabola, as it was hurled back by an unseen hand from behind the number-one pumper. It landed explosively in the middle of the large elderberry bush behind which squatted Patrolman Skelton and his volunteers.

Weeping copiously, Skelton led his small band of followers in a retreat to the far side of Lincoln Street. There he regrouped his forces behind a leafy pair of spiraea bushes and, through eyes streaming tears surveyed the firehouse once more. Through one open window upstairs, he could see a motionless hammock suspended from the ceiling. Whether or not it was occupied, Skelton could not tell. Downstairs, through the open firehouse doors, he saw the number-one ladder truck. Nothing more.

One block away, Donna Prentiss caused a brief halt in Fulton Burrows's progress down the firehouse side of Lincoln Street.

"Kiss me once more, darling," she whispered. And right there, in broad daylight, shielded from the street only by the lush shrubbery that grows everywhere along Lincoln between the sidewalk and the curb, Fulton Burrows complied happily. After a suitable delay, the couple walked on.

Across the street from the firehouse, teller Ezra Donaldson thought he saw something move behind the number-one pumper.

"George, I see one of them," he whispered to Skelton.

"Go on and shoot," Skelton ordered.

Donaldson laid the bank's automatic pistol on the grass.

"Give me one of those rifles," he said.

Al Skidmore surrendered his gun. Ezra sat down on the sidewalk, steadied his elbow on his knee, put the rifle to his shoulder, dropped the front sight into the notch of the rear sight, moved the gun upward toward the firehouse door. His line of sight passed just to the left of the large elderberry hedge that shielded the sidewalk on either side of the firehouse drive.

Ka-pow! went the rifle.

From within the firehouse, a pistol returned the fire. Crack! The first shot shattered a window in the house behind Skelton's group. Crack! Skelton felt a sudden pain in his left chest. Clutching his side, he fell forward heavily.

"They got me," he gasped.

"Why, those..." Ezra Donaldson began. He raised his rifle once more, as two auxiliaries bent helplessly over Skelton.

Al, kneeling beside Ezra, asked, "You see 'em?"

"I think so," Ezra muttered. Actually, since it was very dark inside the firehouse, he couldn't see a thing. He squinted, trying to focus better, trying to see a movement in the dim interior. No, he didn't see anything, but he'd take a shot anyway. He might catch one of the robbers with a ricochet.

Ezra aimed at a shiny fire axe that he could just see on the dark rear wall. He shut one eye, squinted the other nearly shut, began to squeeze the trigger. Unconsciously, he braced for the recoil, completely unaware that in a second and a half Donna Prentiss's curly brown head would emerge from behind the elderberry hedge and enter his sights.

One second passed. Donaldson squeezed harder. The curly head appeared. Al's hand swung upward toward the gun barrel.

Ka-pow!

"What in...?" Ezra Donaldson began, then stared aghast at the boy and girl.

Upstairs in the firehouse, the bullet from Donaldson's deflected rifle entered the open window, where, by the merest chance, it neatly severed one of the two ropes supporting Frisbie Collins's hammock. Collins's body fell to the floor with a resounding thud.

Donna Prentiss, now strolling past the front of the firehouse with Fulton, lifted her pretty eyebrows.

"Did I hear shooting?" she asked.

"Car backfiring," Fulton replied knowingly. He smiled at Donna, who smiled back and clutched his arm a little tighter.

Downstairs in the firehouse, the taller of the two gunmen crouching behind the pumper nervously looked up at the ceiling. He turned to his confederate.

"We're surrounded," he said. "I just heard 'em land someone on the roof."

"How could they land someone on the roof?" said his accomplice.

"Don't ask me, stupid!" the tall man flared. "With a helicopter, maybe!"

The smaller man considered this, then laid his revolver carefully on the floor.

"I'm giving up before I'm shot up," he said.

The tall man once more looked thoughtfully at the ceiling.

Finally, he nodded and also laid down his gun. Together, with hands raised above their heads, the two men stepped forward into the bright April sunlight in front of pumper number one.

"We are yours," the tall man muttered grimly.

At 2:45, the *Daily Sentinel* photographer arrived at the firehouse to take pictures. At 2:51, two state troopers arrived in an unmarked sedan to take the two robbers into custody.

At 3:29, Patrolman Skelton went home, swallowed three

aspirin tablets, and went to bed. It had been discovered earlier, as soon as he could be persuaded to stop clutching his side, that he was really uninjured. His badge had miraculously deflected the bullet. As proof that his dismal early-morning presentiments were completely baseless, Skelton's heroism under fire was noted everywhere and not least in the chambers of the Fry's Landing City Council. Reflect for a moment on what might have happened if Mrs. Skelton *had* remembered to mend the tear in Patrolman Skelton's—that is—Chief Skelton's shirt!

Al Skidmore was also proclaimed a hero for having blocked the gunmen's escape. Consider what might have happened had Al not returned two days early from Boise to make up with Emma.

When Al came up the walk, dirty, disheveled, and on foot (his battered car was still on Benton Avenue with the tire punctured by Skelton's bullet), Emma ran down the stairs and threw her arms around him, embracing the rifle simultaneously.

"Oh, Al, you're safe!" she cried and kissed him madly. "I was so worried."

"Emma, are you all right?" Albert asked. "I couldn't get a thing done in Boise for thinking about you here all alone."

"I'm so glad you're home," Emma cried, squeezing his arm. "I've been so lonely."

"I'll fix that," Al said, swaggering slightly.

"I'm so proud of you, stopping that holdup. Wasn't it lucky you had the rifle with you!"

Al expanded his chest.

At a quarter to five, bank-teller Donaldson phoned his bookie. Five minutes later, he walked to the office of Orville Bascom, president of the bank, knocked, entered, and confessed. He made a clean breast of everything, including the fact that Nineveh, in a race of seven horses, had run seventh.

Orville Bascom shook his gray head sadly. "Well, Ezra," he said, "you leave me no choice of what to do."

"I know, sir," Donaldson said.

Bascom was silent for a moment. "Well," he said, finally, "I suppose all the publicity about your bravery today may help some at your trial."

"I hope so, sir," Donaldson said.

"Although frankly, Ezra," Bascom continued, "I'm appalled, absolutely appalled, at your lack of judgment."

"Yes, sir," Donaldson said.

"That Nineveh!" Bascom said. "He hasn't finished in the money once this year!"

At 5:47, in the living room of their house on Catalpa Road, Marian Burrows told her husband that she smelled smoke.

"You can't, Marian," Fred Burrows said. "I'm not asleep yet."

The truth of the matter was that he smelled smoke, too. Fred stepped out his front door just in time to see his son, Fulton, wearing a suit that badly needed pressing, and sporting a look of dazed glory, walk right past his own front gate as though it didn't exist. Fulton was staring into the eyes of a remarkably attractive young girl.

"Hey, son," Fred Burrows called. "Where've you been? Your mother and I were beginning to worry."

Neither his son nor the pretty girl seemed to see or hear him. Instead, they kept right on walking, hand in hand, smiling at each other in a way that gave Fred Burrows a sudden pang of memory. Maybe, Burrows thought, as he watched them, maybe he understood Fulton a little after all.

After a moment, since he still smelled smoke, he went around to the back of the house, where he was able to trace the smell to the incinerator of his next-door neighbors, Emma and Albert Skidmore. Reaching across the back fence—it was an easy reach, and the curious odor inspired investigation—he lifted the incinerator's pierced metal lid and probed inside with a stick. He came up with a smoldering piece of blue straw that might at one time have been a hat.

He dropped the fragment back, replaced the lid, and walked slowly toward the back of his house, ruminating. As he mounted the back steps, he shook his head and smiled thoughtfully into the gathering dusk. Today Marian had smelled smoke, and there had actually been smoke. Now why in heck, he wondered, should that make him feel so good?

2017, Revisited

Film presented at the Annual Meeting of the 4A's,
(The American Association of Advertising Agencies),
The Greenbrier, West Virginia
April 22, 1967

We open on an extreme close-up of a calendar page. The date reads: 22 April 2095. The date appears to be printed on a transparent acetate sheet.

The camera moves slowly forward, through the calendar page, to reveal the set.

We are looking at the interior of a large cube. The cube's walls, floor, and ceiling are white and translucent. The back wall is a rear projection screen. On it, and continuously throughout the film, a series of pictures change by lap-dissolve—scenes from nature, fashion, art, and elsewhere.

The light increases, and we become aware of the SPOKESMAN. He wears a dark, three-piece suit, and sits in an elegant, transparent chair in the center of the cube. Behind him, the pictures keep changing. No explanation is given as to why the pictures are there, and the SPOKESMAN pays them no attention.

Midpoint in the script the camera moves in for a tight shot of the SPOKESMAN, then reverses its move and pulls back at the same, slow pace.

SPOKESMAN: How do you do.

I'm very grateful for this opportunity to get together and talk about old-time advertising, because...

...as Secretary of Advertising for the U.S. Government...

...the subject is obviously very dear to my heart.

Incidentally, I hope you'll pardon my clothes. There's a fad for wearing period clothing here in the capital...

...in Los Angeles...

...This costume dates back to...oh, about 1967, which, interestingly enough, is also the date of this antique chair.

But I didn't come to talk about clothing or furniture. I came to talk about advertising, as it was back in the year 2017.

I wonder how many of you remember that year, and the marvelous five-day national holiday in honor of the 100th anniversary of the 4A's.

I myself was working for a small agency at the time...

...we had, maybe, 12,000 employees...

...called Hoefer, Dieterich & Brown, up in San Francisco, and I'd like to try to tell you what it was like to be alive in those exciting days, before Interplanetary bought up the last agency, and merged with the U. S. Government.

In 2017, of course, we were living in a total marketing economy. The problems of production had been permanently licked...

...by which I mean to say, of course, that everything was produced in Japan.

The economic question of the hour, in fact, had become simply: "Is the U.S. economy equal to consuming everything the Japanese can turn out?"

Fortunately, we were prepared to meet this challenge. The 4A dream of "more education for advertising" had come true, and the study of advertising was now compulsory...

...from the Fourth Grade right on up through graduation from the Harvard Business School...

...which was also compulsory.

Similarly, the trend toward corporate mergers, which had been clearly evident in the mid-twentieth century, had gone about as far as it could go. There were, in fact, only two companies in the U.S. They were both giant marketing organizations, of course—one was called General Amalgamated, or G.A., and the other was called Chicken Delight Industries.

Although the products these two companies sold were identical—with the exception of the pressure-sensitive label, G.A. or CDI, applied just before the goods left Japan—there was a great deal of healthy competition between them, in accordance with a rather strict set of rules prescribed by the Justice Department.

But enough of economic history. Let's talk about the "Best Ad of 2017."

This calls for a word about media. And while I'm tempted to talk about the early days of intra-cranial radio and the introduction of five-channel living Sense-A-Vision, I would like to talk about a print medium.

As most of you know, beginning in the year 1998, each child was given at birth, by the government...

...in addition to the customary eleven-digit multi-purpose number...

...a subscription to *LIFETIME, the Magazine for YOU.*

LIFETIME was actually half magazine, half newspaper. It was transmitted by laser beam to an electronic device under the kitchen

sink, where it was then printed onto a continuous roll of paper, manufactured from the output of the Disposall.

The editorial content of LIFETIME was unique. That is to say, thanks to automation and the computer, no two copies were exactly alike. The contents varied according to the age, sex, and interests of the subscriber, as recorded and stored in the official Magnetic Memory Cores at the Heptagon.

The advertising content of LIFETIME was also unique. Only those ads that could reasonably be expected to appeal to the subscriber were included in his issue. If an advertiser wanted to reach 28-year-old red-haired mothers of three children—boy, girl, boy—well, that was who they reached.

It was an ideal medium, since it had 100% coverage, no waste circulation, and was...

...no matter how the subscriber might feel about it...

...non-cancelable.

The ad I'm about to show you was judged "Best Ad of 2017" for two chief reasons...

...First, it was, as all good advertising should be, a clear, simple communication about the satisfaction of a great human need.

...And second, because it zeroed in on its market so carefully that it appeared in only *one* subscriber's copy of LIFETIME.

Here it is:

> *HENRY: All is forgiven.*
> *Please come home. I love you.*
> *Elizabeth.*

I suppose there's a message here, and I suppose the message is that advertising, in spite of the laser, the computer, the spaceship...that advertising must always revolve around the needs and desires, the hopes and fears, the strivings and failings of a single individual, and of a universe made up of single individuals.

Even in this advanced day, it's a message worth remembering.

Thank you.

(Camera has now returned to its original position. The lighting dims slowly, the rear projection pictures keep changing until it's too dark to see.)

END

Consequences

I originally titled this chapter *Corkboard Wisdom*. Then I changed my mind.

It wasn't just that *Corkboard Wisdom* sounded smarmy. My real fear was that if anyone liked it I'd be forced to write sequels.

Corkboard Wisdom for the Soul.
Corkboard Wisdom for the Single Parent
The Corkboard Wisdom Cookbook.

So, even though the chapter does deal with corkboards, and even though I allege it contains random scraps of wisdom, I'm playing it safe.

The corkboard that got it all started greets me each time I sit down to write. The back edge of my desk is attached to a wall, the wall is covered with corkboard. The corkboard is covered with family snapshots, stamps, foreign currency, souvenirs, and a lot of items torn from newspapers and magazines.

These items are mostly quotes. I thought they were pretty wise when I push-pinned them up there, and I guess I think they're pretty wise today.

Here's a sample. It's a yellowed newspaper clipping about writing. It reads:

> *"One of the few things I know about writing, is this: Spend it all, shoot it, play it, lose it all right away, every time. Do not hoard what seems good for a later place in the book, or for another book. Give it, give it all, give it now. Something will arise later, something better..."*

A very wise writer named Annie Dillard said that. And that's what I'm going to do. I'm going to take down all the yellowed clippings I've been hoarding on my corkboard, all that accumulated wisdom, and spend it, shoot it, play it, lose it all right now.

The second item from my corkboard concerns writing, too. The late Arthur Kudner, who once headed a big New York advertising agency called, not surprisingly, The Kudner Agency, wrote these words for his son. They got printed somewhere, and I stuck them on my corkboard. Here they are:

> *Never fear big long words.*
> *Big long words name little things.*
> *All big things have little names*
> *Such as life and death, peace and war,*
> *Or dawn, day, night, hope, love, home.*
> *Learn to use little words in a big way.*
> *It is hard to do,*
> *But they say what you mean.*
> *When you don't know what you mean –*
> *Use big words.*
> *That often fools little people.*

While we're rubbing elbows with advertising people, let me toss in an item from the once-mighty, now-even-mightier J. Walter Thompson Agency. I found it long ago in the conference room of some now-forgotten company. Let's call it XYZ Corp.

Three agencies were making presentations to handle the XYZ account—ours, J. Walter Thompson, and some third agency. Our presentation came last, following JWT's. As we were setting up our slide and movie projectors, I saw a stray booklet lying on the conference table. It was a copy of JWT's "leave-behind".

What's a leave-behind? It's a booklet agencies hand out after a presentation to remind the XYZ's of this world about the agency's superb qualifications, its "unique fit" with XYZ Corp. (whether

XYZ makes shaving cream or submarines), and its eagerness to get to work!

But this was *JWT's* leave-behind! I felt I had found the Rosetta Stone. *"Everything You Wanted to Know About A Big-Time Agency But Were Afraid to Ask."*

I slipped the booklet into my briefcase.

Later, back at the agency I eagerly read my purloined document. This is what I learned: (1) JWT's leave-behind contained a standard amount of routine puffery. (2) JWT's leave-behind contained no secrets. (3) JWT's leave-behind was only slightly more boring than our own.

It did, however, contain the following piece of advice:

Be persistent as well as brilliant.
Nothing in the world can take the place of persistence.
Talent will not; nothing is more common than unsuccessful
    men with talent.
Genius will not; unrewarded genius is almost a proverb.
Education will not; the world is full of educated derelicts.
Persistence and determination alone are omnipotent.
Press on.

We didn't get the XYZ account, but I tore these JWT words out of their booklet and push-pinned them to my corkboard. At various times I've given copies to our children. They'll probably tell you I've done it dozens of times. This only shows I got the message about persistence.

Back to the corkboard. Here's another piece of borrowed wisdom.

"The trivial errors of other people do not always require your preoccupation or correction."

Funny how it's always *other* people whose errors need correcting. The quote is from my friend Mike Friedman, famed research cardiologist. You met him earlier in a restaurant where he and I sent back a flawless bottle of wine just to see what would happen.

Mike introduced the term "Type A behavior" in his 1974 best-seller, *"Type A Behavior and Your Heart."* The principal symptoms of Type A behavior—for starters anyhow—are impatience and hostility. Mike's landmark research project, which preceded his book and involved thousands of subjects, indicated that Type A behavior was a principal cause, maybe even *the* principal cause of heart disease.

Type A's, Mike found, were especially bothered by those *"trivial errors of other people."* Colleagues and underlings seldom came up to scratch. The home team at ball games, the visiting team, the umpires, the hot dog vendor, all had annoying flaws. At the home dinner table, Type A's ate fast and never lingered. While there, however, they found plenty of aggravating defects in spouses and children that cried out for correction. No wonder they were Type A! They were driven to it!

Type B's, Mike found, were much less likely to suffer these problems. Type B's were considerably less time-urgent, less hostile, less critical, less affected by the daily aggravations that sent Type A's into orbit. And less likely to have coronaries.

Mike wrote a sequel, still in your bookstore, called "Treating Type A Behavior and Your Heart." Besides offering important self-help strategies for reducing your chance of heart attack, it also delivers an unexpected gift: Lessons in how to become a decent human being. Have a look.

For me, the perfect self-help book is a novel. I almost never read a novel that does not in some way help me calibrate the way I live my life.

Don't get me wrong. I don't read novels looking for moral instruction. I read them because I *like* reading novels. They engage me, they entertain me, they take me on trips into other lives, other countries, other centuries. They let me look in on living rooms and boardrooms and bedrooms I'd never otherwise see. Any moral lessons come as a bonus.

I like reading the work of new novelists whose work is hot off the press, and I also like writers whose work has been tested by time. People like Thackeray, Trollope, Jane Austen. I enjoy their stories, their humor, their irony and satire, and I find their works full of lessons about the human condition.

Times have changed a lot since those days of lamplight and carriages, but we still live very much in the world of Becky Sharp and Septimus Harding and Elizabeth Bennet. We meet people from that world every day. We see them on the freeway, in the mall, at the movies, on television.

They look like ordinary people—programmers, cab drivers, shoe salesmen, stock brokers. They drive Fords, they drive Ferraris, they smoke, they don't smoke, they drink three Cosmopolitans before dinner, they only drink Evian, they drink gallons of red wine because it's good for their hearts. They use cell phones, they work out at health clubs. They're as contemporary as you can get.

However...change their costumes, rewind their 2003 vocabularies back to 1813, and they all come straight out of *Pride and Prejudice*.

When I was in college I used to worry that after I read all those great authors, I'd be out of luck. I'd have no more good books to read.

My fears have proved groundless.

Still, every now and then I find myself wondering, what shall I read next? Which of the zillion books in my local library or in bookstores or in the New York Times Book Review, which is really worth reading?

I have an answer pinned to my corkboard. It's a page I copied from the World Almanac. It lists the winners of the Nobel Prize for Literature since 1901, the first year the prize was given. That year it went to a Frenchman, Rene F. A. Sully Prudhomme. The list continues—with six years out for two World Wars—up to the present.

If you should copy the list, the first thing to do is put a red mark in front of the names of authors whose work you've already read. You'll probably find you've read more Nobel winners than you thought. Then comes the pleasure of deciding which Nobel laureate you'll read next. They've all been stamped with the *Nobel Seal of Approval*, so it's unlikely you'll get a klunker.

Here's another way to find good stuff to read. Take a look at the winners of the Booker Prize. I found the list on the internet—it goes back to 1938—and stapled it to the Nobels.

The Booker, or as it's now known, the Man Booker Prize, is awarded each year to the "best novel of the year written by a citizen of the British Commonwealth or the Republic of Ireland." That's not as parochial as it may sound. The old Commonwealth stretches a long way around the globe.

Then there's the Booker shortlist. Each year's winner is selected from a list of six finalists, who are in turn honed down from a much larger list. A novel that makes it into the final six is at least worth a try.

My other source of great learning is the movies. There are more truly fine movies than you might suspect, and they are filled with memorable, sometimes painful but almost always enjoyable lessons in living. I don't go for the lessons. I go because I *love* movies. The lessons just come tagging along.

Take *Grand Canyon.*

I suppose that's my favorite movie. If you haven't seen it, you've missed a treat.

The movie takes place in modern-day Los Angeles. Mack (Kevin Kline) is an immigration lawyer. Mack's friend Davis (Steve Martin) produces slasher movies. Simon (Danny Glover) is a tow-truck driver who saves Mack's life. Mary McDonnell, Alfre Woodard, and Mary-Louise Parker play other key roles, and Lawrence and Meg Kasdan provide the script. The result is moving and often funny, filled with a lot of wry wisdom about honesty, friendship, luck, love, coincidence, and the possibility of miracles.

Grand Canyon also contains its own lesson about the importance of movies.

Here's the scene. We're on a movie lot, and Mack and Davis have just had lunch in the studio commissary. They are now riding back to Davis's sound stage in his glitzy golf cart. Mack is driving because Davis is recovering from having been shot in the leg by a mugger who took his Rolex.

In an earlier scene Davis has had a mystical in-hospital experience. It was revealed "unto him" that he should give up making violent movies, and from that day forward make only serious, socially-conscious films. Mack asks him why, therefore, he has gone back to making movies in which the "money shot" shows a bus driver's brains being splattered across a windshield.

DAVIS:

I regained my senses. I was talking like a moron.

Look, Mack, I'm an artist. Now, you go ahead and laugh, because everybody does. Nobody in this town will admit that a producer is an artist.

The cart passes a man walking between sound stages:

DAVIS:

Hi, how y'doin?

But I know what I do. I know how many lame-o directors I've had to carry on my back every step of the way and then watch as they take all the glory and reviews and awards...

MACK:

Which awards were they?

DAVIS:

That's okay. I don't mind working in modest anonymity. That's the way Thalberg did it, too.

MACK

If they're so lame-o, why do you hire them?

DAVIS:

Because I haven't got time to do it myself—hanging around

the set all day doing that boring lighting and shit. Let them do that. That's beside the point. The point is...

DAVIS sees a pretty woman walking in the opposite direction.

DAVIS:

Turn around and go back down there...

Where was I?

MACK:

"The point is..."

DAVIS:

The point is, there's a gulf in this country, an ever-widening abyss between the people who have stuff and the people who don't have shit...

...it's like this big hole has opened up in the ground, as big as the fucking Grand Canyon, and what's come pouring out...

The cart catches up with the pretty woman.

DAVIS:

Hi, my name's Davis. I'm in Building 78, the whole building. You should stop by—I think I have something for you...

As the cart moves on:

This is the greatest town on Earth! Go left here. Where was I?

MACK:

Grand Canyon?

DAVIS:

Yeah, and what's come out of this big hole is an eruption of rage, and the rage creates violence, and the violence is real, Mack, and nothing's going to make it go away until someone changes something, which is not going to happen...

...and you may not like it. Even I may not like it, but I can't pretend it isn't there, because that is a lie, and when art lies it becomes worthless.

So, I gotta keep telling the truth, even though it scares the shit out of me, like it scares the shit out of you, even if it means some motherfucker can blow a big old hole in my leg for a *watch*...and I'm going to walk with a fucking limp for the rest of my life, and consider myself lucky...

That's what's amazing, you know, it's what we count as lucky today. I mean, our criteria for lucky has changed a bit...

MACK:

Davis, we're not talking about great art here...

DAVIS:

Says you, Mr. Snob, Mr. Arbiter of Taste, Mr. Immigration Lawyer to the Arts...

I'll tell you this, though. There's so much rage going around, we're damn lucky we have the movies to help us vent a little of it...

MACK:

Oh, that line is so tired! I'm shocked you'd use it...

DAVIS:

You think anyone can do what I do? You think just anyone can make the crap I make?

MACK:

Wasn't there something about life force, or life affirming? Something like that. That's what Claire told me...

DAVIS:

This *is* life, pal, that's what I'm trying to get through your big, sanctimonious skull...

There's always been violence, there will always be violence, violence and evil and men with big guns.

My movies reflect what's going on, they don't *make* what's going on. And if I happen to make them better than any one, then I've got a bigger responsibility than anyone to serve it up.

DAVIS gets out of the cart and starts walking towards his sound stage. He turns back to MACK, still in the cart.

DAVIS:

Mack, you ever see the movie called *Sullivan's Travels*?

MACK:

No...

DAVIS:

That's part of your problem, you know, you haven't seen enough movies. All of life's riddles are answered in the movies. It's the story about a man who loses his way. He's a filmmaker, like me, and he forgets for a moment just what he was set on earth to do.

Fortunately, he finds his way back. That can happen, Mack. Check it out.

MACK watches as DAVIS, leaning on his cane, limps toward an immense sliding door that opens to receive him. He goes in, the door reverses, closing slowly with a deep, muffled boom.

I empathize with Davis. I've seen hundreds of movies, *Sullivan's Travels,* comedies, tragedies, dramas, horror films, sci-fi. I've never reached the point, however, where I didn't need to see more, more of these entertaining answers to life's riddles.

I confess to being a movie junkie, and I confess to being a fiction junkie. In no way, however, am I ready for detox. So what do I get in return for all the time I spend in a dark theater, or with my feet on the coffee table, reading yet another novel?

A couple of years ago Adair Lara, a gifted writer whose column appears—not often enough—in the *San Francisco Chronicle,* helped me answer that question. Naturally I tore her words out of the newspaper, and pinned them you know where.

Let me quote her.

"I was on my afternoon walk, musing about my last book club meeting, in which we talked about 'Madame Bovary.'

It occurred to me that I am 46, and that when I die, all my slender knowledge of the misadventures of Madame Bovary will die with me. And it will have done me no earthly good in the meantime.

"Yet somehow it seems worth doing, just as for some reason this walk in the flickering afternoon light seems worth taking, though I gain nothing by it.

"My friend Georgia explained it to me by e-mailing me a passage from Henry James' 'The Tragic Muse.' After some discussion, a character asks why we bother increasing our capacity for appreciating the good in life.

"Where are the fine consequences?" he asks peevishly.

"In one's own spirit. One is oneself a fine consequence,' the other replies serenely.

"Which explains to me why I can read Flaubert and then have Madame Bovary in my head as an end in itself.

"I am myself a fine consequence."

That's my excuse, too. I'm not wasting time going to movies and devouring novels. I'm solving the riddles of the world. Just for me. I am myself a fine consequence.

This raises a question. As I sit writing the last lines of this final chapter, how do I weigh up all the fine consequences since I started writing fiction in my converted Sonoma doghouse?

I'm glad to have had consequences of the kind Adair Lara refers to, ones that come from hours spent with fascinating books or in movie houses filled with popcorn smells and flickering images. I treasure each of those hours.

I'm glad, too, that I still derive pleasure from what seems to be my continuing need to write things down. This book is evidence that I do.

Truly significant consequences, of course, do not come from books or movies or writing, but from people. Foremost in my life is my best friend Mary-Armour, to whom, many pages earlier, I dedicated this book. Then comes the family we created and raised together, and the families they are in turn creating and raising. Then come our friends, our true, loving, valuable friends.

Taken all together, these are very fine consequences indeed.

KILLING DAVE HENDERSON, ETC...

JAMES NELSON

Part Three: Partners in Crime

A Lot of People...

A lot of people helped me get this baby on the road, and I am grateful to all of them.

That goes double, no, triple for my long-time friend and colleague, John De Bonis. John designed the book, made endless layouts, and offered creative suggestions of all kinds. Working with John is always enjoyable and frequently involves food, which is a good thing in itself. I am greatly in his debt.

I also want to thank my much newer friend, Dr. Ali Kianfar. When Ali is not lecturing on Islamic History and Sufism at Stanford or the University of California, he operates Phoenix Word & Press. Phoenix turned my words and John's layouts into pages ready to print. Thank you, Ali, for all your help.

Richard Harris, ace production art director, fine-tuned everything so Roger Rapoport, who heads RDR Books, could publish it in all its present magnificence. I thank them both very much.

Nathaniel Wing, son of my first literary agent, is a professor of French at Louisiana State University. He provided me not only with a new Virginia cousin—his wife, Elizabeth Nelson Wing—but also with the snapshot of his father that faces page 57. Thanks, Nat.

In Toronto, Janette Ewen of *Chatelaine* helped in my attempt to track down Jack Bush, whose fine illustration accompanies my story *The Trouble with Ada*. Alas, we couldn't find him. I am grateful to Jack Bush anyway, and to Janette for her friendly help, and for permission to reprint *Chatelaine's* cover.

Lucie Prinz is another friendly magazine person. She hails from *The Atlantic Monthly*, and I thank her for her permission to reprint an *Atlantic* cover. Unfortunately, I could not locate Carl Rose, whose wonderful line drawings accompanied *Elect the*

Healthiest in *Atlantic*. They accompany it again in this book, and I thank Carl Rose.

Garry Trudeau was easy to find, and very gracious when I did. He added a touch of class to my book by letting me reprint his magnificent drawing of Mike Doonesbury walking past a snowbound bicycle on the Yale campus. Thank you, Gary. I also thank Mark Alden Branch and the *Yale Alumni Magazine* for letting me reprint the cover on which Garry's drawing appeared.

Will Park is another talented artist to whom I owe thanks. Will's illustrations of Dave Henderson set the tone for my Henderson piece when it ran in *Smithsonian*. In this book they continue their unique contribution to the Henderson legend.

I owe thanks to another artist, my good friend and college classmate, Curtis Fields. Curt designed a handsome blazer patch for the 50th reunion of our class, and okayed its use opposite the first page of *Meeting Dave Henderson*.

I thank several people for the chapter titled *On Beyond Henderson*. First is Heather Killebrew Cowdery. Heather filled me in on the doings of several fascinating but totally bogus Dartmouth graduates who turned up year after year in the *Dartmouth Alumni Magazine*.

Sylvia Babcock Warner of St John, V.I., also has my thanks. Without Sylvia there would never have been a Nadie Jones Doesmith. Without Nadie the alumni notes of Sylvia's class at Garrison Forest School would have been ordinary instead of fascinating. Thanks, Sylvia, for letting me use Nadie's story. Thanks also to Crystal Lee of Garrison Forest School, for helping me find Sylvia.

Bernie Huebner deserves his own special medal. Bernie filled me in on reports, startling and totally ersatz, that found their way into alumni histories at Harvard for several decades. You will find Bernie's amazing narrative in *On Beyond Henderson*. To add even more luster to this opus I would like to thank our former Ambassador to France, Walter Curley. Walter let me include one of the many notes he wrote about his totally fictitious Yale classmate Larry Vaughn.

I also make a deep bow to Sheila Shiki y Michaels. Sheila's reports on her exotic family added spice to many a William & Mary class notes column. Looking back, Sheila says her real life turned out to be even stranger than the one she invented.

Emilie Rissman is a professor of biochemistry & molecular genetics at the University of Virginia. So far as I know she has never tampered with her class notes. She did, however, e-mail me a very nice picture of her father, Arthur Rissman, which accompanies my chapter about him. Many thanks, Emilie.

I also thank my niece Jill Nelson who searched Denver alleys to find and photograph the city's last remaining ashpit. Not an easy task. Thanks, Jill, and thanks also for the Ascension Church photo.

I also thank my friend Joe Friedman for searching his family archives to come up with pictures for the chapter about his famous father.

Jenny Graham of *The Philadelphia Inquirer* gave me permission to reprint the cover of the *Sunday Magazine* in which *My Private War With Herman* appeared. I thank her as well as the talented Alex Stein who illustrated the story. I searched, but couldn't find him.

Sarah Scrymser is the managing editor of *Good Housekeeping*. I thank her for letting me reprint the cover of the issue in which *April 14th in Fry's Landing* appeared. I also thank Alex Ross, the illustrator, another gifted artist I could not find.

Tom Sylla is an artist in a different field: Film. I found him quite easily, perhaps because he happens to be my son-in-law. Tom took my short film, *2017 Revisited*, and converted its into the digital pictures that accompany the script. Thanks, Tom.

Andy Bandit of *20th Century Fox* has my thanks for giving permission to use a still and part of the script for the movie *Grand Canyon*. I also thank Steve Unversagt of Art Instruction, Inc. for searching his company's archives to find samples of its *"Draw Me"* matchbooks.

Al Hart is my friend and agent, the man who sold the Dave Henderson epic to *Smithsonian*. I am grateful to Al, not just for selling my stuff in the past, but for his gamble on finding a publisher for this book.

I have admired Adair Lara's writing in *The San Francisco Chronicle* for a long time. I am pleased she gave me permission to quote at length from one of her wise and candid columns. Thank you, Adair.

I swore I would never write the words "last but not least," and I'm still trying not to fall into that trap. This is, however, my last acknowledgment, and my thanks are going to someone who is most certainly not the least. She is, in fact, the most.

I am referring, of course, to Mary-Armour, my buddy, editor, critic, fan club, wife, and all-around best friend. She was there when every word of this stuff was written. Her enormous contribution to this book is spread across all its pages.

Thanks, Shorty.

San Rafael, California
December, 2006